THE USE OF HERBICIDES IN THE FOREST - 1986

by

J S P Sale

*Silviculturist, Forest Research Station, Alice Holt Lodge
Wrecclesham, Farnham, Surrey GU10 4LH*

P M Tabbush

*Silviculturist, Northern Research Station, Roslin
Midlothian EH25 9SY*

and

P B Lane

*Forestry Commission Work Study Team, Eastern Region,
Santon Downham, Brandon, Suffolk IP27 OTJ*

PREFACE

Since 1954 the Research Division has issued a chatty domestic newsletter called *Entopath news* two or three times a year. Produced by the Entomology and Pathology Branches, it has served to keep Forestry Commission staff aware of the latest developments and recommendations in forest protection.

In 1963, to help the practising forester to keep abreast of the rapidly changing use of chemicals and new materials becoming available, a special *Entopath news chemical control supplement* was brought out. This gave a comprehensive account of the practical use of herbicides, insecticides and fungicides. The supplement was revised every two or three years and subsequently chemicals for wildlife control and fertilising were added.

In 1979 the revision was called *The use of chemicals in the Forestry Commission*. In 1983, in response to requests from field staff, it was decided to separate herbicides from the other chemicals and to produce a revised version of recommendations for the use of herbicides in the forest (Forestry Commission Booklet 51) when necessary. The use of other chemicals is covered by a companion volume revised rather less frequently (Forestry Commission Booklet 52). Information on the use of herbicides in the nursery, an increasingly specialist subject in view of the reduction in the number of forest nurseries, will be presented in a subsequent publication.

The authors of this Booklet wish to acknowledge their indebtedness to their predecessors for much past research work and for the presentation of information in the former titles quoted above.

Although produced primarily for internal use by FC staff, all these publications have been made available to the private forestry sector. It should be noted that the information and recommendations given are relevant to conditions in the Forestry Commission's forests, and no responsibility can be taken for treatments applied elsewhere.

CONTENTS

1. INTRODUCTION

1.1 Purpose and format

1.1.1 This is the first revision of the original 1983 edition of this Booklet and incorporates recent developments in herbicides, equipment and methods of application.

Further revisions will be produced (and re-issued to FC recipients) as frequently as is necessary to keep the Booklet up to date and useful as a working manual.

1.1.2 Content and layout

The diagnosis of weed problems is not covered in detail. The assumption is made that the reader will have an adequate general knowledge of forest management and an appreciation of other non-herbicidal methods of weed control against which to weigh the treatments recommended here.

Likewise application techniques cannot be adequately condensed into a Booklet of this size. Such expertise is covered in the training of managers and operators (see Section 9.1).

The layout of the Booklet is given in the List of Contents. Sections 3 to 8 cover each of the main weed types. Each section contains a brief description of the main problems encountered followed by a list of recommended herbicides. Each herbicide then enjoys a full entry describing its use on that weed type.

Herbicide entries are set out in a standard format with which it is hoped the reader will become familiar: descriptions of approved products, properties, toxicity and crop tolerance lead on to recommendations for application rates, methods and timing, followed by notes on limitations of use, safety precautions and protective clothing.

Sections 9 to 11 contain very important information and details upon which the success of any herbicide treatment depends. PLEASE READ THEM CAREFULLY AND FOLLOW THEIR GUIDANCE whenever you undertake a programme of weed control with herbicides.

1.2 Nomenclature of herbicides

Herbicides are from time to time referred to by one of the following different types of name: e.g. for glyphosate,

Chemical name: N-(phosphonomethyl) glycine
Common name: Glyphosate
Product name: Roundup (which is in fact a liquid formulation of the mono (isopropylamine) salt of glyphosate containing the equivalent of 360 g/l of glyphosate).

6

The chemical name is normally complex and hard to remember. It is abbreviated for industrial and commercial purposes into the common name. It is around the common name that the stock of information on properties and uses of the herbicide is assembled. For marketing purposes and to meet particular weeding situations, one or more products will be developed, sometimes all with identical chemistry but often based on a variety of different salts or esters of the active ingredient (the herbicide itself). It is the individual product formulation which is the subject of scrutiny and eventual clearance (for safety) by the Pesticide Safety Precautions Scheme (PSPS) and subsequent approval (for efficacy) by the Agricultural Chemicals Approval Scheme (ACAS). Any change in the formulation of a cleared or approved product must be referred to PSPS and ACAS for further clearance and approval respectively.

1.3 **Regulation of pesticides and pesticide use**
Voluntary arrangements which have operated up to 1986 are to be replaced by a statutory system.

1.3.1 **Non-statutory regulations**
For nearly 30 years the Pesticides Safety Precautions Scheme (PSPS) has been the principal mechanism for evaluating the safety of pesticides in the UK. The Scheme, which is a formally negotiated agreement between the agrochemical industry and the Government, subjects each product intended for sale in the UK to a rigorous assessment. Only those products which satisfy these searching tests are cleared for distribution to the public. Clearance may be subject to various constraints, eg mode of application or amount of protective clothing required. It is Forestry Commission policy to use only products which have been thus shown to be safe.

Recommendations for safe use of cleared products are given on the labels, and are also published in the form of loose-leaf Recommendation Sheets. A copy of the current Sheet for any particular chemical can be obtained from the Ministry of Agriculture, Fisheries and Food, Pesticides Branch, Great Westminster House, Horseferry Road, London SW1P 2AE.

Proprietors of cleared products could, if they wished, submit their product for assessment under the Agricultural Chemicals Approval Scheme (ACAS). Only those products deemed to fulfil the claims of efficacy made on their label were granted Approved Product status and included in the annual publication *Approved products for farmers and growers* (Reference Book 380).

Because of the small size of the forestry market a manufacturer may have chosen not to apply for approval under ACAS specifically for forestry. This does not, however, preclude the use of these chemicals in the forest. Such herbicides are only recommended here when they have proved their value and effectiveness over a considerable period of general use in the forest, or have been tested experimentally against specific forest weed conditions.

1

ACAS is now closed for the consideration of new products, but the 1985 edition of *Approved products for farmers and growers* will continue to be available until replaced by a new publication under the statutory system. It can be obtained (£4.25 a copy) from the Ministry of Agriculture, Fisheries and Food, (Publications), Lion House, Willowburn Trading Estate, Alnwick, Northumberland NE66 2PF (Telephone Number 0665 602881), or from the main offices of the Agricultural Departments of Scotland and Northern Ireland. It contains much information on the safe use of pesticides and lists the pesticides which are subject to the Poisons Rules.

APPROVED PRODUCT LABELS
CARRY FULL INSTRUCTIONS FOR USE
ALWAYS READ THE LABEL

1.3.2 **Statutory approval of pesticides**
Part III of the Food and Environment Protection Act 1985 made provision for new Regulations which (as this edition goes to press) are expected to come into operation later in 1986. These Regulations will build on and reinforce the controls hitherto exercised under PSPS and ACAS, converting the old voluntary arrangements into a fully fledged statutory system.

The mode of operation of the statutory system is not expected to differ greatly from previous practice except that minor and small scale uses of pesticides (including a number in forestry) will need to be registered as off-label uses if they are not mentioned on product labels.

BEFORE YOU USE A HERBICIDE - READ THE LABEL
It has been designed for your protection

1.4 **British Agrochemical Supply Industry Scheme Ltd (BASIS)**
In March 1978 a registration scheme for the Distribution of Crop Protection Products was launched with the following objectives:

1. Ensuring a high standard of safety in the distribution (and application) of crop protection products.

2. Ensuring that staff at any level engaged in the handling of crop protection products are competent and belong to establishments and organisations with people having specialised knowledge of their safety and efficacy.

3. Promoting and encouraging the safe and efficient usage of such products by professional users in agriculture, horticulture and forestry with due regard to the environment.

All products cleared by the PSPS (except rodenticides and wood preservatives) are covered by the scheme. A 'distributor' is any individual, company or organisation retailing or applying under contract crop protection products for professional use in agriculture, horticulture or forestry.

1

A list of registered distributors can be obtained from:

The Secretary, BASIS Ltd., Bank Chambers, 2 St John Street, Ashbourne, Derbyshire DE6 1GH.

1.5 **Poisons Rules**
Certain products are subject to the provisions of the Poisons Act 1972 and the Poisons List* and Poisons Rules* made under it. These regulations include general and specific provisions for the labelling, storage and sale of scheduled poisons. Any products governed by these rules are marked in the list of manufacturers and distributors of approved products (Section 12) or can be found in the *Approved products for farmers and growers* handbook (see Section 1.3.1 above).

At present, the only herbicide on the Poisons List recommended in this Booklet is paraquat. All the other chemicals are relatively safe materials. It must be remembered however that most herbicides are poisons to a greater or lesser degree. It is essential therefore when using them to follow a code of practice which ensures:

(a) effective weed control
(b) safety of operators, other staff and the public
(c) the absolute minimum of harm to the environment.

Before using herbicides the information given in this Booklet must be understood and all safety precautions meticulously observed.

* Obtainable from HMSO.

1.6 **The Poisonous Substances in Agriculture Regulations 1984†**
Users of the rather more poisonous chemicals included in these Regulations are required by law to observe certain precautions. They should obtain a copy of the official booklet *A guide to The Poisonous Substances in Agriculture Regulations 1984*, HS(R)20*, which fully explains the requirements. Products governed by these Regulations can be found in the *Approved products for farmers and growers* handbook (see Section 1.3.1 above). None of the herbicides currently recommended in this Booklet is listed under these Regulations.

* HMSO.
† Statutory Instrument 1984 No.1114 available from HMSO

9

2. WEED CONTROL IN THE FOREST

2.1 The need to weed

MUCH WEEDING CAN BE AVOIDED BY GOOD MANAGE-MENT PRACTICE. Cultivation is the main method of weed control on most upland afforestation sites and if planting is prompt and successful no other weed control will be necessary. Many restocking sites are initially weed-free and are not ploughed or scarified but the need to weed can still be avoided by planting before weeds have reinvaded. On certain very fertile and weedy sites, the quantity of weed seed may be such that a fallow period is desirable after felling to allow the weeds to germinate. Pre-planting weed control (by chemicals or by cultivation) should then have an effect which will last while the trees become established.

The main objective of weeding is to secure rapid early growth and the even and successful establishment of the stand. This is achieved by the elimination of competition for light, moisture and nutrients. Competition for light can be relieved by chemical or mechanical means, the former being generally the cheaper option. The elimination of root competition for moisture and nutrients can only be achieved with the use of herbicides. It is particularly important to ensure that grass roots do not compete with tree roots at planting and during the ensuing months by applying herbicides before or immediately after planting to a spot or band at least 1.0 m in width.

Weed control may also be necessary to prevent the spread of particular perennial weeds, e.g. Rhododendron, or for the purposes of access or fire protection.

2.2 Assumptions and conventions used in this Booklet

(See also Section 13 for glossary and list of abbreviations.)

2.2.1 Area

Throughout this Booklet, unless the context clearly indicates otherwise, all references to areas (usually hectares) refer to TREATED AREA, that is the area of ground or plantation that is actually covered with herbicide.

2.2.2 Crop tolerance

The descriptions of crop tolerance assume average site conditions, healthy crop trees (prior to treatment) and the application of herbicide at recommended rates and times and by the recommended methods.

The manager should bear in mind that crop tolerance (and weed susceptibility) is very much affected by a whole range of factors (site, crop condition, provenance, weather, season, etc). He should proceed with caution in choosing herbicides and rates until he is confident of the local conditions within which he is working.

10

Most selective herbicides are also total herbicides if applied at an excessive rate. Your crop is at risk if you overdose.

2.2.3 Pre- and post-planting

In most cases differences between pre- and post-planting recommendations are small or non-existent. The presence of a crop among the weeds is simply a further constraint which may make it necessary to reduce the dose rate to a level where the crop is unaffected (or at least any herbicide damage is acceptable), or require careful placing of the herbicide to ensure crop trees are not affected.

For each herbicide entry, the paragraph on toxicity contains a statement of how rapidly the herbicide is broken down in the soil. Where appropriate there is also a note of any necessary waiting period after treatment with the herbicide and before it is safe to plant on the site.

2.2.4 Application rates

Where two rates (or a range of rates) are given, use the higher rate for pre-planting and non-crop situations. Use the lower rate among crop trees unless the weeds include some species which are moderately resistant to the herbicide. If such weeds are present, consider whether the application rate can be increased without harm (or at least without unacceptable damage) to the crop.

2.3 Application patterns

It is usually easier and quicker to apply herbicide as an overall complete treatment, but this economy of effort imposes maximum stress on the herbicidal tolerance of the crop and the surrounding ecosystem and normally uses more herbicide than is strictly required for effective weed control.

Placed or directed application patterns are more demanding of time and skill but minimise the amount of herbicide used, the stress to which the crop is subjected and the impact on wildlife.

The manager should carefully consider which application pattern best suits his weeding requirements among the options of complete (incremental), band (over-row or inter-row) or spot (with or without tree guard) application.

2.4 Application methods

The applicator used to apply a herbicide will depend upon the nature of the herbicide (granular or liquid) and on the application pattern required. For liquids, the dilution rate selected (and hence the total volume to be applied) will also affect the choice of applicator. The higher cost of granules, the water and weight saving of lower volume liquid applications and the simplicity of direct applicators are factors to be borne in mind here. Section 11 gives

2

detailed guidance on these aspects. Handheld and tractor mounted applicators are described. Aerial application is not covered but should be considered by any manager with a large programme of work using any herbicide which is cleared for aerial application. The herbicidal principles of aerial application are just the same as for ground based applications but of course only overall treatments are possible.

FC managers contemplating an aerial programme using any herbicide other than asulam (which is cleared for aerial use) should consult Silviculture Division, Edinburgh, via their Conservator for guidance and permission. Non-FC managers may wish to seek advice from the appropriate Forestry Commission Conservancy Office.

2.5 **Additives**

At present the use of additives is mentioned only once in these recommendations and this relates to ammonium sulphamate (Section 8.2). Other additives which may enhance the activity of certain herbicides are under trial but no recommendation can yet be made.

2.6 **Safe disposal of surplus herbicides**

The best approach to adopt is to ensure that no surplus herbicide is left behind after a weeding programme. It is much better to leave a small area untreated (to be tidied up later by handweeding or deferred to next year) than to over purchase and be left with unusable surplus.

If herbicides do become surplus, consider the following options listed in order of preference:

(i) Incorporate them in the next season's programme (see Section 9.3 for storage precautions).

(ii) Invite the supplier to collect unopened containers which are still in good condition.

(iii) Spray the herbicide on to a suitable stretch of plantation or non-crop ground where some weeding benefit may accrue and where no risk of damage exists.

(iv) Enlist the service of a reputable chemical disposal firm.

(Note: FC managers will of course seek re-allocation of surpluses to other units. Approval for destruction of stocks must be obtained before arranging disposal.)

NEVER tip surpluses into mineshafts, quarries, watercourses, lakes or any drainage channel.

ALWAYS observe all safety instructions on the herbicide label.

For further guidance, obtain and read the following MAFF Booklet:

B2198 *Guidelines for the disposal of unwanted pesticides and containers on farms and holdings* (1984).
Available free from MAFF (Publications), Lion House, Willowburn Estate, Alnwick, Northumberland NE66 2PF.

2

2.7 References for further reading
Several references to other published books and leaflets are to be found in the appropriate Sections of this Booklet.

The following titles will also be useful for background reading and to provide fuller detail of some aspects of herbicide practice:

Forestry Commission Publications:

Bulletin 48: *Weeding in the forest,* 1974.
Booklet 40: *Chemical control of weeds in the forest,* 1975.
Leaflet 62: *Ultra low volume herbicide spraying,* 1975.
Leaflet 64: *Control of heather by 2,4-D,* 1976.

Other publications:

Weed control handbook:
Principles (seventh edition, 1982) edited by H A Roberts
Recommendations (eighth edition, 1978) edited by J D Fryer and R J Makepeace

FC Internal Memoranda (for FC staff only):

Silvicultural Memorandum 3 (revised 1985)
Silvicultural Memorandum 43 (revised April 1983)
Relevant Work Study reports.

Note: Because of the rapid evolution of herbicide practice, all the quoted literature should be read with due regard to the date of publication.

2.8 The decision chain - a summary
The following sequence briefly describes the assessments and decisions involved in achieving correct application of a liquid herbicide. The sequence for a granular herbicide is similar but with rather fewer variables to reconcile.

Using Sections 3 to 8:

1. From crop and weed characteristics, determine the choice of suitable herbicides, dose rates and application patterns.

2. Consider any other factors limiting the choice of herbicide, applicator, drop size, dilution rate or diluent.

3. Select a suitable: herbicide
dose rate
applicator
droplet size (if critical)
application pattern and method
approximate dilution rate

2

and thence the intended overall volume of liquid to be applied per treated hectare.

Using Section 11:

4. Calculate the likely equipment requirements and settings, choosing values for the relevant variables, e.g. for the knapsack sprayer:

nozzle size
spray pressure
dilution

to give a convenient walking (or tractor) speed for the operator.

5. Calibrate the equipment on a small test area by setting up as calculated above and check the resulting application rate.

6. Adjust the variables to achieve the correct application rate.

3. GRASSES AND GRASS/BROADLEAVED WEED MIXTURES

3.1 General

Competition by grasses and broadleaved herbs in a young plantation can seriously reduce the survival and early growth of the crop and lead to an extended establishment period. Grasses especially can compete vigorously for water and light and effective control is often crucial to successful crop growth.

As forest weeds, grasses can be grouped into two categories: coarse grasses which are generally tall, bulky, rank, stiff, rhizomatous and often tussocky and others which in contrast are known as soft grasses. Soft grasses are generally more susceptible to herbicides while coarse grasses usually show a somewhat greater resistance (see Table I).

There are six herbicides recommended for grass control:

ATRAZINE (various trade products)
ATRAZINE with DALAPON (Atlas Lignum)
GLYPHOSATE (Roundup)
HEXAZINONE (Velpar)
PARAQUAT (Gramoxone 100)
PROPYZAMIDE (Clanex or Kerb)

Their effectiveness varies according to the weed species present and the season of the year. The susceptibility of the more important grasses to these herbicides is given in Table I.

Perennial rhizomatous grasses are the most difficult to control and require the use of residual herbicides or foliar contact herbicides which are translocated to the rhizomes.

Residual herbicides remain active in the soil and are absorbed through the roots. They can be inactivated by the presence of organic matter in the soil. Hexazinone and dalapon, however, retain some residual activity on peat soils while atrazine can be used as a foliage spray since it has both residual and contact action.

Propyzamide has purely residual action and is not recommended for use on soils with a peat layer more than 10 cm in depth. By contrast glyphosate and paraquat have contact action only and their use is therefore independent of soil type.

Because peat soils are water-retentive, moisture competition is not so severe and the need for weeding is generally less than on mineral soils.

All the herbicides will have some effect on broadleaved herbs but wherever these constitute a significant part of the weed population glyphosate and paraquat (and perhaps hexazinone) are more likely to give good results.

The following decision tree will assist in selecting a suitable herbicide according to season, crop species and weed type.

3

1.

Pre-planting

Spring	Summer/Autumn	Winter
ATRAZINE/DALAPON HEXAZINONE	GLYPHOSATE	†PROPYZAMIDE

2.

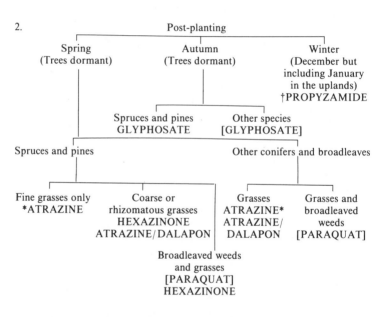

Post-planting

Spring (Trees dormant) — Autumn (Trees dormant) — Winter (December but including January in the uplands) †PROPYZAMIDE

Spruces and pines GLYPHOSATE — Other species [GLYPHOSATE]

Spruces and pines — Other conifers and broadleaves

Fine grasses only *ATRAZINE — Coarse or rhizomatous grasses HEXAZINONE ATRAZINE/DALAPON — Grasses ATRAZINE* ATRAZINE/ DALAPON — Grasses and broadleaved weeds [PARAQUAT]

Broadleaved weeds and grasses [PARAQUAT] HEXAZINONE

* ATRAZINE has no soil activity in soils with an organic peaty layer and only controls grasses. *Molinia caerulea, Calamagrostis epigejos* and *Deschampsia caespitosa* are resistant.

† PROPYZAMIDE is not recommended for soils with more than 10 cm of peat nor for the control of *Dactylis glomerata, Holcus mollis* or *Calamagrostis epigejos.*

Note: Square brackets indicate that crop trees must be protected from direct contact with the herbicide.

TABLE I   SUSCEPTIBILITY OF COMMON GRASSES IN THE FOREST TO RECOMMENDED HERBICIDES

Herbicide and rate (kg ai/ha) Grass species		Atrazine 4-6 kg/ha	Atrazine & Dalapon 4+4 kg/ha	Hexazinone 1.8 kg/ha	Glyphosate 0.5 kg/ha	Paraquat 1.0 kg/ha	Propyzamide 1.5 kg/ha
Agropyron repens (Couch grass)	(C)	MR	MS	S	S	MR	S
Agrostis spp. (Bent grasses)		S	S	S	S	MS	S
Anthoxanthum odoratum (Sweet vernal)		S	S	S	S	MS	S
Arrhenatherum elatius (False oat)	(C)	MR	S	S	S	MS	S
Calamagrostis epigejos (Small reed grass)	(C)	R	-	MS	MS	R	R
Dactylis glomerata (Cocksfoot)	(C)	MR	MR	S	S	MR	MR
Deschampsia caespitosa (Tufted hair grass)	(C)	MR	MR	MS	S	MS	S
Deschampsia flexuosa (Wavy hair grass)		S	S	S	S	S	S
Festuca arundinacea (Tall fescue)		MS	S	S	S	MS	S
Festuca pratensis (Meadow fescue)		MS	S	S	S	MS	S
Festuca ovina (Sheep's fescue)		S	S	S	S	MS	S
Festuca rubra (Red fescue)		S	S	S	S	MS	S
Holcus lanatus (Yorkshire fog)		S	S	S	S	MS	S
Holcus mollis (Creeping soft grass)		MR	-	S	S	MR	MS
Molinia caerulea (Purple moor grass)	(C)	R	-	S	S	S	S
Poa annua (Annual meadow grass)		S	S	S	S	MS	S
Poa pratensis (Smooth meadow grass)		MS	S	S	S	MS	S
Poa trivialis (Rough meadow grass)		S	S	S	S	MS	S
Juncus spp. (Rush)		R	MS	MS	S	S	R

S   = Susceptible: control should be excellent
MS = Moderately susceptible: control should be adequate
MR = Moderately resistant: control may be inadequate
R   = Resistant: little effect or control obtained
(C) = Coarse grasses (all others can be considered as soft grasses)

3

3.2 ATRAZINE

Approved products

50% w/v liquid (water soluble concentrate):
>Atraflow (Burts & Harvey)
>Gesaprim 500L (Ciba-Geigy)

Description

Atrazine has both foliar contact action and soil action. It is most useful on soft grasses (see Table I) but of limited use against herbaceous broadleaved species and the coarse grasses (unless applied at higher rates than recommended below).

Atrazine has no soil activity in soils with an organic peat layer.

Toxicity

Atrazine has a low mammalian toxicity and is slightly toxic to fish. It has a low solubility in water and is slow to break down in the soil, remaining active for over 6 months.

Planting can be carried out immediately after treatment.

Crop tolerance

Conifers: all are tolerant to overall application except NS, WH and EL which are sensitive during the growing period from April to June.

Broadleaves: all are sensitive while in leaf and should only be treated during dormancy in spring.

Rates and methods of application

Liquid: applied at 10 litres of product per treated hectare (5 kg ai/ha) in water through the following applicators:

(a) Knapsack sprayer at MV (200 - 300 l/ha).
(b) Knapsack sprayer with 'VLV' nozzle at LV (60 - 130 l/ha).
(c) Herbi at VLV (10 - 20 l/ha).
(d) Tractor mounted boom sprayer at MV (200 - 300 l/ha).
(e) Tractor mounted Ulvaforest at VLV (10 - 20 l/ha).
(f) Drenchgun for spot application at LV (30 - 60 l/ha).

Refer to Section 11 for details of applicator and correct calibration.

Date of application

February to May. February and March applications usually give the best results. Applications in May and June will give effective weed control but also slight crop damage (and severe damage to the more sensitive species NS, WH and larch; see above).

Limitations

1. *Holcus mollis,* although a soft grass, is not readily controlled.
2. Do not use atrazine on NS intended for Christmas trees.

3. Crops on light calcareous or sandy soils and also on heavy waterlogged sites seem to suffer more damage from atrazine. On these sites application rates should be reduced and atrazine should not be used again the following year.
4. No soil activity on soils with an organic peat layer.

Safety precautions
Wash hands before meals, before attending to personal needs and at the end of the day's work.

Read Section 9. In particular observe the standard precautions and working practice outlined in Section 9.3.

Ensure that operators and supervisors are trained in the necessary skills and have the relevant Forest Safety Guides.

The label on the herbicide container has been designed for your protection - ALWAYS READ THE INSTRUCTIONS ON THE LABEL.

Protective clothing
See table of Protective Clothing Required (Section 10) for the clothing appropriate to the method of application selected. Please note the special requirements when handling and mixing concentrates.

3

3.3 ATRAZINE WITH DALAPON
Approved product
10%+10% w/w granules: Atlas Lignum (Atlas Interlates Ltd).
Note: This product was previously named Herbon Lignum.

Description
A mixture of atrazine and dalapon in granular form. The mode of action is similar to that of atrazine alone (see Section 3.2) but the inclusion of dalapon extends its activity to coarse grasses and peat soils. Late summer applications may control some broadleaved weeds.

Toxicity
Atrazine has a low mammalian toxicity and is slightly toxic to fish. It has a low solubility in water and is slow to break down in the soil, remaining active for over 6 months.

Dalapon has a very low mammalian toxicity and a low toxicity to fish. It is broken down by soil micro-organisms in less than 3 months.

Planting can be carried out immediately after treatment.

Crop tolerance
SS, SP, LP, GF, NF and RC are tolerant.

NS, CP, DF, larches, WH and broadleaves are rather more sensitive. Application rates for these species should not exceed 30 kg of the product per treated hectare.

Rate and method of application
40 kg of product per treated hectare (4 kg of each ai/ha), or 30 kg if sensitive crop species are present (see Crop tolerance above), are applied through a pepperpot or Moderne applicator.

Refer to Section 11 for details of applicators and correct calibration.

Date of application
Mid March to May before flushing is the optimum period. Earlier applications may be effective if there is active grass growth. June to August applications will be less effective and the dalapon component will cause damage if it sticks to the tree foliage.

Limitations
1. *Calamagrostis epigejos* is likely to be resistant.
2. Even application of granules is essential to avoid crop damage.
3. Do not use Atlas Lignum on NS intended for Christmas trees.

Safety precautions
Wash hands before meals, before attending to personal needs and at the end of the day's work.

Read Section 9. In particular observe the standard precautions and working practice outlined in Section 9.3.

Ensure that operators and supervisors are trained in the necessary skills and have the relevant Forest Safety Guides.

The label on the herbicide container has been designed for your protection - ALWAYS READ THE INSTRUCTIONS ON THE LABEL.

Protective clothing
See table of Protective Clothing Required (Section 10) for the clothing appropriate to the application of granules.

3

3

3.4 GLYPHOSATE
Approved product
36% w/v liquid: Roundup (Monsanto).

Description
A translocated herbicide taken up by the foliage and conveyed to the roots. It causes chlorosis and eventual death of leaves and inhibits growth of roots and shoots.

Glyphosate controls a wide range of weeds including grasses, broadleaved herbs, bracken, heather and woody weeds. When applied late in the growing season, the main effect is obtained in the following year.

Toxicity
Glyphosate has a low mammalian toxicity and is harmful to fish. On contact with the soil it is very quickly broken down. Planting can be carried out immediately after treatment.

Crop tolerance
SS, NS, SP, CP, LP, RC and LC: will tolerate overall sprays provided leader growth has hardened. Hardening can occur as early as the end of July or may be delayed until October in some locations and seasons. To avoid damage to lammas growth, herbicide sprays must be directed away from leaders. During the active growing season trees must be guarded or the spray placed to avoid contact with the crop.

DF: as above but rather more sensitive.

Broadleaves and larch: will not tolerate overall applications; always use a guard, a weedwiper or a placed spray to avoid contact with the crop.

Rates of application
1. *Sprays*
    Upland Britain: 2.0 litres (0.72 kg ae/ha).
    Lowland Britain: 1.5 litres (0.54 kg ae/ha) of product per treated hectare diluted in water to a total volume appropriate for the applicator and method selected.
2. *Direct application*
    One part of product diluted in 6 parts of water through a direct applicator.

Methods of application
1. Handheld overall spray
    (a) Knapsack sprayer for band application at MV (200 - 300 l/ha), or with 'VLV' nozzle at LV (60 - 130 l/ha).
    (b) Drenchgun for spot application at LV (30 - 60 l/ha).

2. Tractor mounted spray
   (a) Boom sprayer for complete or band application at MV
       (200 - 400 l/ha).
   (b) Ulvaforest for complete or band application at VLV (10
       - 20 l/ha).

3. Handheld placed spray
   (a) Knapsack sprayer (with guard if required) at MV (200
       -300 l/ha).
   (b) Knapsack sprayer with 'VLV' nozzle at LV (60 -
       130 l/ha).
   (c) Herbi at VLV (10 -20 l/ha).

4. Direct application
   (a) Weedwiper Mini for spot application at VLV (20 - 40
       l/ha uncalibrated).

Refer to Section 11 for details of applicators, nozzles, flow rates and correct calibration.

Date of application
Glyphosate can be applied at any time of year when vegetation is actively growing but is most effective when applied from July to September.

Direct application achieves maximum control when the vegetation is actively growing and under 0.3 m in height. In taller vegetation and where a large number of seed heads are present the degree of control will be reduced.

Glyphosate applied later than June will be too late to lessen the effects of weed competition in the current season.

Limitations
1. Diluted glyphosate may denature after 2 to 3 days. Where possible use tap water as the diluent and only mix sufficient for the day's programme.
2. Glyphosate is most effective on moist vegetation when relative humidity and air temperatures are high.
3. Heavy rainfall within 24 hours of application may reduce the herbicide's effectiveness by preventing sufficient foliar absorption.

Safety precautions
Wash hands before meals, before attending to personal needs and at the end of the day's work.

Read Section 9. In particular observe the standard precautions and working practice outlined in Sections 9.3.

Ensure that operators and supervisors are trained in the necessary skills and have the relevant Forest Safety Guides.

The label on the herbicide container has been designed for your protection - ALWAYS READ THE INSTRUCTIONS ON THE LABEL.

Protective clothing

See table of Protective Clothing Required (Section 10) for the clothing appropriate to the method of application selected. Please note the special requirements when handling and mixing concentrates.

3

3.5 **HEXAZINONE**
Approved product
24% w/v liquid: Velpar Liquid (Selectokil).

Description
A residual translocated herbicide which has some foliar contact action but is primarily taken in through the roots. Hexazinone controls a fairly wide range of grasses and some broadleaved weeds, and is effective on organic soils.

Toxicity
Hexazinone has a low mammalian toxicity but is classed as an EYE IRRITANT. It has a very low solubility and a very low toxicity to fish. In soil it is slowly broken down by microbial action.

Planting of tolerant species can be carried out immediately after treatment but, because of its slow breakdown, it is not appropriate for pre-planting treatment if susceptible species are to be used.

Crop tolerance
SS, NS, SP, CP and LP: will tolerate overall sprays provided leader growth has hardened (approx. July onwards). During the active growing season trees must be guarded or the spray placed to avoid contact with the crop.

All other species: susceptible to hexazinone and must not be treated.

Rates and methods of application
Applied as 7 litres of product per treated hectare (1.68 kg ai/ha) through the following applicators:
(a)   Knapsack sprayer (with a guard if required) in water at MV (not less than 250 l/ha). A large diameter flood jet nozzle and low pressure should be used to avoid the production of fine droplets.
(b)   Drenchgun for spot application at LV (30 - 60 l/ha).
Because it is an eye irritant, hexazinone is not cleared for application at ULV.

Refer to Section 11 for details of applicators, nozzles, flow rates and correct calibration.

Date of application
Hexazinone is effective if applied from mid-February to August but best results are achieved by April-May applications. The presence of a crop limits overall application to early spring and the period after shoot growth has ceased (see Crop tolerance above).

Safety precautions
As hexazinone is an eye irritant special care must be taken during mixing and application.

Wash hands before meals, before attending to personal needs and at the end of the day's work.

Read Section 9. In particular observe the standard precautions and working practice outlined in Section 9.3.

Ensure that operators and supervisors are trained in the necessary skills and have the relevant Forest Safety Guides.

The label on the herbicide container has been designed for your protection - ALWAYS READ THE INSTRUCTIONS ON THE LABEL.

Protective clothing
See table of Protective Clothing Required (Section 10) for the clothing appropriate to the method of application selected. Please note the special requirements when handling and mixing concentrates. WEAR A FACE SHIELD WHEN HANDLING AND APPLYING THIS HERBICIDE.

3.6   PARAQUAT
Approved product
20% w/v liquid: Gramoxone 100 (Plant Protection).

Description
A contact herbicide which disrupts the photosynthetic process of the aerial parts of plants. It is partly translocated. Paraquat controls a wide spectrum of weeds and its contact action can be seen within a day of spraying.

Toxicity
Paraquat has a high toxicity to mammals and its use is subject to the Poisons Rules (Poisons Act 1972). It is readily soluble in water but has a low toxicity to fish. In soil paraquat is rapidly inactivated. Keep farm stock away from the treated area for at least one day. Leave at least three days between spraying and subsequent planting.

Crop tolerance
All tree species are sensitive to paraquat and must be protected during spraying. Weed foliage must be treated before it has become tall enough to brush against crop trees after paraquat application.

Rates and methods of application
Applied as 5 litres of product per treated hectare (1 kg ai/ha) diluted in 200 - 400 litres of water through the following applicator:
> Knapsack sprayer at MV using FLOOD JET AND LOW PRESSURE so that no fine droplets are produced. The largest diameter jet must be used.

Because paraquat is poisonous no other method of application can be recommended.

Refer to Section 11 for details of applicators, nozzles, flow rates and correct calibration.

Date of application
At any time of year to green growing vegetation. Best results are obtained by early spring or early autumn application during dull weather.

Limitations
1.   Regrowth of rhizomatous and stoloniferous grasses can be expected.
2.   NEVER apply paraquat through a mistblower or by any method producing fine droplets.
3.   Use clean water to make up diluted material. Peaty or muddy water will inactivate paraquat by adsorption on to organic or clay particles.

Safety precautions
THE POISONS RULES APPLY TO PARAQUAT: see Section 1.5 and also Silvicultural Memorandum 3.

Wash hands before meals, before attending to personal needs and at the end of the day's work.

Read Section 9. In particular observe the standard precautions and working practice outlined in Section 9.3.

Ensure that operators and supervisors are trained in the necessary skills and have the relevant Forest Safety Guides.

The label on the herbicide container has been designed for your protection - ALWAYS READ THE INSTRUCTIONS ON THE LABEL.

Protective clothing

See table of Protective Clothing Required (Section 10) for the clothing appropriate to the method of application selected. Please note the special requirements when handling and mixing concentrates. In addition WEAR A FACE SHIELD AND RESPIRATOR WHEN HANDLING AND APPLYING THIS HERBICIDE.

3.7 PROPYZAMIDE

Approved products

4% w/w granules: Clanex (Shell).

Kerb Granules (PBI).

15% w/v suspension concentrate: Clanex Liquid (Shell).

50% wettable powder: Kerb 50W (PBI).

Description

A soil acting herbicide which slowly volatilises in cold soil and is taken up by germinating weeds and through the roots of existing weeds, especially grasses. Herbaceous broadleaved weeds which emerge in late season will not be controlled. Early species may be partially controlled.

Toxicity

Propyzamide has a very low mammalian toxicity although the wettable powder is classed as a mild eye irritant. It is slightly soluble in water and has a low toxicity to fish. It slowly breaks down in the soil, lasting for 3-6 months.

Planting can be carried out immediately after treatment.

Crop tolerance

All commonly planted tree species are tolerant.

Rates and methods of application

Granules: applied at 37.5 kg of granules per treated hectare (1.5 kg ai/ha) through the pepperpot or Moderne applicator.

Suspension concentrate: applied at 10 litres of product per treated hectare (1.5 kg ai/ha) in water (if required) through the following applicators:

(a) Knapsack sprayer at MV (200 - 300 l/ha).
(b) Knapsack sprayer with 'VLV' nozzle at LV (60 - 130 l/ha).
(c) Herbi at VLV (undiluted).
(d) Tractor mounted boom sprayer at MV (200 - 300 l/ha).
(e) Tractor mounted Ulvaforest at VLV (undiluted).
(f) Drenchgun for spot application at LV (30-60 l/ha).

Wettable powder: applied as 3 kg of wettable powder per treated hectare (1.5 kg ai/ha) in water through the following applicators:

(a) Knapsack sprayer at MV (200 - 300 l/ha).
(b) Herbi at VLV (20 l/ha).
(c) Drenchgun for spot application at LV (30-60 l/ha).

For best results mix the dry powder into a smooth paste with a small amount of water, slowly add more water, stirring all the time, until the mix is sloppy, then add the remaining water up to full dilution.

Refer to Section 11 for details of applicators, nozzles, flow rates and correct calibration.

3

Date of application
Apply during October to December (January can be included in upland Britain).

Limitations
1. Although propyzamide can be used very effectively for pre-planting applications, the effect of the herbicide applied in winter cannot often be seen by the time of normal planting.
2. Organic soils decrease the activity of propyzamide and treatment of soils with a greater depth of peat than 10 cm is not recommended.
3. The following grasses show some resistance to propyzamide:
    Dactylis glomerata
    Holcus mollis
    Calamagrostis epigejos.

Safety precautions
Wash hands before meals, before attending to personal needs and at the end of the day's work.

Read Section 9. In particular observe the standard precautions and working practice outlined in Section 9.3.

Ensure that operators and supervisors are trained in the necessary skills and have the relevant Forest Safety Guides.

The label on the herbicide container has been designed for your protection - ALWAYS READ THE INSTRUCTIONS ON THE LABEL.

Protective clothing
See table of Protective Clothing Required (Section 10) for the clothing appropriate to the method of application selected. Please note the special requirements when handling and mixing concentrates.

4. BRACKEN

4.1 General

Bracken competes strongly with young trees for light during the latter part of the growing season. At the end of the year it collapses and can smother and flatten small trees with its weight, increasingly so if snow lies on top of them both. Bracken is rarely sufficiently advanced in spring to afford protection from frosts and is not worth retaining for this purpose. Weeds which take over from bracken can usually be equally easily controlled by chemicals but if this is not the case it may be advantageous to retain partial bracken cover by hand or mechanical weeding in bands or spots.

Ploughing does give some control of bracken but on sites where bracken is most vigorous the stems on either side of the plough ridge will overgrow conifers.

If a crop is present, chemical control must be followed by hand cutting before the fronds collapse on to the trees and cause damage. Whenever possible, herbicide should be applied pre-planting to avoid this problem.

The herbicides used for bracken control are:

ASULAM (Asulox).

GLYPHOSATE (Roundup).

These chemicals both control the rhizomes of bracken and prevent or retard further growth of fronds the following season.

Asulam gives slightly better control of bracken but no other weeds are controlled. Conifer tolerance is high.

Glyphosate gives adequate control but can cause damage to the crop particularly if it is used in mid-summer. If bracken is mixed with other weeds (e.g. brambles) then glyphosate should be chosen for its wide spectrum of weed control.

4

4.2 **ASULAM**
Approved product
40% w/v liquid: Asulox (May & Baker).

Description
Asulam is a contact herbicide which is taken up by the foliage and translocated to the rhizomes. Growth of the bracken is then retarded or fails entirely the following season. Control may last from 1 to 4 years or more, depending on the rate applied and the date of application.

Toxicity
Asulam has a very low mammalian toxicity and a very low toxicity to fish. It is fairly quickly broken down in the soil, losing half its biological potency in about 10 days.

Crop tolerance
All conifers except WH: mature trees are tolerant of recommended rates but young trees may show slight chlorosis and check at the highest rates and earliest dates of application.

WH: somewhat more sensitive but will tolerate up to 7 litres of product per hectare during August and early September.

Beech, birch, elm and poplar: as for conifers.

Other broadleaves: susceptible. Trees should be protected by a guard or the spray directed to avoid the crop.

Rates and methods of application
Applied as 5 litres (early season) - 10 litres (late season) of product per hectare (2 -4 kg ae/ha) diluted in water through the following applicators:

Overall application
(a) Knapsack sprayer at MV (200 - 300 l/ha).
(b) Knapsack sprayer with 'VLV' nozzle at LV (60 - 130 l/ha).
(c) Mistblower at LV (90 -175 l/ha).
(d) ULVA at VLV (10 - 20 l/ha).
(e) Tractor mounted Ulvaforest at VLV (10 - 20 l/ha).
(f) Aerial.

Refer to Section 11 for details of applicators, nozzles, flow rates and correct calibration.

Date of application
Late June to August. Best results are obtained by application just as the frond tips have unfurled and formed an almost complete canopy. Treatment at this stage may reduce the need to hand-cut the dead stems at the end of the growing season.

The later in the season application is made the higher is the rate of asulam required to obtain control.

Limitations

1. A minimum of one month should elapse after treatment before cutting the bracken down or ploughing the ground.
2. Access for spraying should be made by pushing fronds aside and not by cutting.
3. Do not spray if rainfall is expected within 24 hours.
4. Prolonged drought may render the bracken unreceptive to foliage-applied herbicide.

Safety precautions

Wash hands before meals, before attending to personal needs and at the end of the day's work.

Read Section 9. In particular observe the standard precautions and working practice outlined in Section 9.3.

Ensure that operators and supervisors are trained in the necessary skills and have the relevant Forest Safety Guides.

The label on the herbicide container has been designed for your protection - ALWAYS READ THE INSTRUCTIONS ON THE LABEL.

Protective clothing

See table of Protective Clothing Required (Section 10) for the clothing appropriate to the method of application selected. Please note the special requirements when handling and mixing concentrates.

4.3 **GLYPHOSATE**
Approved product
36% w/v liquid: Roundup (Monsanto).

Description
A translocated herbicide taken up by the foliage and conveyed to the rhizomes. It causes chlorosis and eventual death of fronds and inhibits regrowth.

Glyphosate controls a wide range of weeds including grasses, broadleaved herbs, bracken, heather and woody weeds. It is thus particularly effective for bracken in mixture with these other weed types. On bracken some dieback of foliage can be expected in the year of application. In the following season rhizomes fail to send out fronds.

Toxicity
Glyphosate has a low mammalian toxicity and is harmful to fish. On contact with the soil it is very quickly broken down. Planting can be carried out immediately after treatment but note Limitation 5 below.

Crop tolerance
SS, NS, SP, CP, LP, RC and LC: will tolerate overall sprays provided leader growth has hardened. Hardening can occur as early as the end of July or may be delayed until October in some locations and seasons. To avoid damage to lammas growth, herbicide sprays must be directed away from leaders. During the active growing season trees must be guarded or the spray placed to avoid contact with the crop.

DF: as above but rather more sensitive.

Broadleaves and larch: will not tolerate overall application: always use a guard or a placed spray to avoid contact with the crop.

Rates and methods of application
Applied as 2.0 litres of product per hectare (0.72 kg ae/ha) diluted in water through the following applicators:

Overall application
(a)   Knapsack sprayer at MV (200 - 300 l/ha).
(b)   Knapsack sprayer with 'VLV' nozzle at LV (60 - 130 l/ha).
(c)   Mistblower at LV (90 -175 l/ha).
(d)   ULVA at VLV (10 - 20 l/ha). For full effect, dilute the herbicide with at least 5 times the volume of water.

If broadleaved weeds such as bramble are also to be controlled, the rate must be increased to 3.0 litres of product per hectare.

Placed spray
(a)   Knapsack sprayer (with guard if required) at MV (200 - 300 l/ha) or with 'VLV' nozzle at LV (60 - 130 l/ha).

Refer to Section 11 for details of applicators, nozzles, flow rates and correct calibration.

Date of application
July to August inclusive after frond tips have uncurled but before senescence. Glyphosate works best when weeds are actively growing.

Limitations
1. Diluted glyphosate may denature after 2 to 3 days. Where possible use tap water as the diluent and only mix sufficient for the day's programme.
2. Glyphosate is most effective on moist vegetation when relative humidity and air temperatures are high.
3. Access for spraying should be made by pushing the fronds aside and not by cutting.
4. Heavy rainfall within 24 hours of application may reduce the herbicide's effectiveness by preventing sufficient foliar absorption.
5. A minimum of one month should elapse after treatment before cutting the bracken down or ploughing the ground.
6. On bracken mixed with woody weeds, mistblowing is usually the most effective of the hand-held methods but it is also likely to inflict a higher degree of damage on unhardened crop trees.
7. Prolonged drought may render the bracken unreceptive to foliage-applied herbicide.

Safety precautions
Wash hands before meals, before attending to personal needs and at the end of the day's work.

Read Section 9. In particular observe the standard precautions and working practice outlined in Section 9.3.

Ensure that operators and supervisors are trained in the necessary skills and have the relevant Forest Safety Guides.

The label on the herbicide container has been designed for your protection - ALWAYS READ THE INSTRUCTIONS ON THE LABEL.

Protective clothing
See table of Protective Clothing Required (Section 10) for the clothing appropriate to the method of application selected. Please note the special requirements when handling and mixing concentrates.

5. HEATHER
5.1 General

On sites where the availability of mineral nitrogen limits tree growth, and where the dominant vegetation is heather (*Calluna vulgaris*), nitrogen deficiency may develop in certain species of conifer. This may need to be alleviated by complete spraying to kill the heather.

Sitka spruce is by far the most important species in this context and unless otherwise stated all the recommendations given here relate to it. NS, WH, GF, NF, DF and CP may also be severely checked by heather competition.

The need to control heather can often be avoided by:
(a) planting a non-susceptible species,
(b) burning the heather before ploughing,
(c) restocking felled areas before the heather has time to invade, or
(d) planting spruce in mixture with SP, larches or LP.

Herbicides recommended for heather control are:
   2,4-D ESTER (Silvapron D (for ULV) and various emulsifiable concentrates (for MV application)).
   GLYPHOSATE (Roundup).

2,4-D ester is the generally recommended herbicide. It can be used selectively during the growing season although at the rates required to kill heather some damage is to be expected to the crop.

Glyphosate can be used in late season when trees are dormant and this may provide the best means of controlling heather amongst trees less than 1 metre in height. Glyphosate does not taint water and has a very low mammalian toxicity and may therefore be the best choice for water catchment areas. Glyphosate is also likely to cause some damage to crop trees at the rates required to give a good heather kill.

5.2 **2,4-D ESTER**
Approved products
ULV formulation
40% w/v: Silvapron D (BP).
Emulsifiable concentrate of a low volatile ester
50% w/v: BASF 2,4-D Ester 480 (BASF).
50% w/v: Chafer 2,4-D Ester (Chafer).
50% w/v: Destox (Campell (Sales)).
50% w/v: BH 2,4-D Ester 50 (Burts & Harvey).

Description
2,4-D is a plant growth regulating herbicide to which many herbaceous and woody broadleaved species are susceptible. It is absorbed mainly through aerial parts of the plant but also through the roots. Because of the oil-based formulation, applications of 2,4-D ester are relatively rainfast. The hormonal activity browns the heather shortly after treatment but exhibits its full effect in the following season.

5

Toxicity
2,4-D has a moderate mammalian toxicity but is harmful to fish (see Section 9.4.1). It is broken down in the soil within 30 days.

There is a risk to bees through ingestion when spraying heather in flower. This can be minimised by good liaison with bee-keepers.

One month should elapse between treatment and subsequent planting.

Crop tolerance
SS, NS and OMS are moderately tolerant.
SP, CP, DF, RC, GF and NF are rather less tolerant.
LP, WH and larches are sensitive.
Broadleaves are very sensitive to 2,4-D.

Hot weather at the time of spraying may increase crop damage.

Rates and methods of application
1. ULV formulation applied without dilution through the ULVA or the tractor mounted Ulvaforest at rates as shown in the following table:

Area	Soil type	Mid-July to Mid-August	Second half of August
Northern Britain	Peat	10 litres/ha	12 litres/ha
	Mineral	15 litres/ha	16 litres/ha
Southern Britain	All sites	10 litres/ha	12 litres/ha

The mean tree height should be at least 1 metre to prevent contact between the spray and the leading shoots.

When the ULVA is used the spray should be applied with the spray head at about 45 degrees to the ground.

As an alternative, the Herbi can be used but the level of heather control achieved is lower than with ULV equipment. On the other hand crop tolerance is better because the spray can be more easily directed. Inter-row spraying with the Herbi can therefore begin as early as May or June (at the same rates as for mid-July), increasing the rates in the above table by 25% to achieve an effect equivalent to that of the ULVA.

2.   Emulsifiable concentrates applied at the following rates of 50% w/v product per hectare:

Soil type	May	June to mid-August	Second half of August
Peat	10 litres	8 litres	10 litres
Mineral	12 litres	10 litres	12 litres

The appropriate volume of emulsifiable concentrate is applied in water through the following applicators:

(a)   Knapsack sprayer at MV (200 - 300 l/ha).
(b)   Knapsack sprayer with 'VLV' nozzle at LV (60 - 130 l/ha).
(c)   Mistblower at LV (90 - 180 l/ha).

Date of application
See tables in preceding paragraph but note that application earlier than mid-July should only be applied through a knapsack sprayer as a directed spray so as to avoid serious crop damage.

Limitations
Special precautions are required in WATER CATCHMENT AREAS to avoid water taint - see Section 9.4.
Leader damage is more likely to occur on trees less than 1 m tall.

Safety precautions
SEE SECTION 9.5 for special precautions for operators using 2,4-D.
Wash hands before meals, before attending to personal needs and at the end of the day's work.
Read Section 9. In particular observe the standard precautions and working practice outlined in Sections 9.3.
Ensure that operators and supervisors are trained in the necessary skills and have the relevant Forest Safety Guides.
The label on the herbicide container has been designed for your protection - ALWAYS READ THE INSTRUCTIONS ON THE LABEL.

Protective clothing
See table of Protective Clothing Required (Section 10) for the clothing appropriate to the method of application selected. Please note the special requirements when handling and mixing concentrates.

5.3 GLYPHOSATE
Approved product
36% w/v liquid: Roundup (Monsanto).

Description
A translocated herbicide taken up by the foliage and conveyed to the roots. It causes chlorosis and eventual death of leaves and inhibits growth of roots and shoots.

Glyphosate controls a wide range of weeds including grasses, broadleaved herbs, bracken, heather and woody weeds. The herbicidal effects take some time to develop on heather and the full response is not evident until the following growing season.

Toxicity
Glyphosate has a low mammalian toxicity and is harmful to fish. On contact with the soil it is very quickly broken down. Planting can be be carried out immediately after treatment.

5

Crop tolerance
Spruces and pines are moderately tolerant to overall sprays of glyphosate after new growth has hardened. Hardening can occur as as early as the end of July or may be delayed until October in some locations and seasons. Leaders should not be sprayed if at all possible, especially when lammas growth occurs. Other species should not be sprayed.

Rates and methods of application
(i)   On mineral soils: 6 litres of product per hectare (2.2 kg ae/ha),
(ii) On peaty soils: 4 litres of product per hectare (1.4 kg ae/ha),
applied in water as a placed spray through the following applicators:
(a)   Knapsack sprayer at MV (200 - 300 l/ha).
(b)   Knapsack sprayer with 'VLV' nozzle at LV (60 - 130 l/ha).
(c)   Herbi at VLV (20 l/ha).
(d)   Tractor mounted Ulvaforest at VLV (10 - 20 l/ha).

Refer to Section 11 for details of applicators, nozzles, flow rates and correct calibration.

Date of application
Late August to end of September after new growth on crop trees has hardened.

Limitations
1.   Diluted glyphosate may denature after 2 to 3 days. Where possible use tap water as the diluent and only mix sufficient for the day's programme.
2.   Glyphosate is most effective on moist vegetation when relative humidity and air temperatures are high.

3.   Heavy rainfall within 24 hours of application may reduce the herbicide's effectiveness by preventing sufficient foliar absorption.

4.   While bees are unaffected by glyphosate, heather flowering will probably be affected by applications earlier than August. Beekeepers should be advised not to site hives on areas to be sprayed.

Safety precautions

Wash hands before meals, before attending to personal needs and at the end of the day's work.

Read Section 9. In particular observe the standard precautions and working practice outlined in Section 9.3.

Ensure that operators and supervisors are trained in the necessary skills and have the relevant Forest Safety Guides.

The label on the herbicide container has been designed for your protection - ALWAYS READ THE INSTRUCTIONS ON THE LABEL.

Protective clothing

See table of Protective Clothing Required (Section 10) for the clothing appropriate to the method of application selected. Please note the special requirements when handling and mixing concentrates.

5

6. WOODY WEEDS

6.1 General

This group of weeds contains a wide range of species including brambles, climbers, shrubs and all types of tree but does not include waxy-leaved evergreens such as rhododendron (see Section 8). The dividing line between weeds and crop plants is frequently unclear and requires a precise definition of management objectives and constraints (such as the present and future amenity effects of broadleaved components of a stand).

Their biological similarity to crop trees can make selective chemical control difficult or impossible. As perennial woody plants, many with the ability to coppice strongly, they present a complex of weeding situations requiring a variety of control methods.

Herbicides recommended are:
AMMONIUM SULPHAMATE (or AMS) (Amcide) - frill girdle, notch, cut stump.
2,4-D AMINE - tree injection
FOSAMINE AMMONIUM (Krenite) - foliar spray.
GLYPHOSATE (Roundup) - foliar spray, tree injection, cut stump.
2,4,5-T - foliar spray, basal bark, frill girdle, injection, cut stump.

6.2 Types of treatment

Control methods fall into three groups:
Foliar treatment (Fosamine ammonium, glyphosate or 2,4,5-T).
Stem treatment (a) Basal bark spray (2,4,5-T).
(b) Frill girdling, notching and tree injection (AMS, 2,4-D, glyphosate or 2,4,5-T).
Cut stump treatment (AMS, glyphosate or 2,4,5-T).

Foliar treatment
This is normally the preferred method of application wherever the weeds are in leaf and the foliage is accessible to be sprayed. Costs per hectare are usually relatively low. Tall stems which need to be cut and cannot for some reason be stump treated may be allowed to regrow for 1 or 2 years before spraying. Table II gives an indication of the susceptibilities of various species to the recommended herbicides.

6

TABLE II

SUSCEPTIBILITY OF WOODY SPECIES TO FOLIAR APPLICATION

Species	HERBICIDE RATES		
	Fosamine 2.4 kg ai/ha	Glyphosate 1.08 kg ae/ha	2,4,5-T 3.5 kg ae/ha
Acer campestre	MR/MS	MS	MS
Acer pseudoplatanus	MR/MS	MS	MS
Alnus spp.	S	(-)	S
Betula pendula	S	S	S
Betula pubescens	MS	MS	MS
Cornus sanguinea	MS/S	(-)	MS/S
Corylus avellana	MS/S	MS	MS
Fraxinus excelsior	MS	S	MR
Ligustrum vulgare	S	S	MS
Populus tremula	MS/S	S	S
Prunus laurocerasus	R	(-)	MR
Prunus spinosa	S	S	MS
Quercus (robur/petraea)	MS/S	MS	MR/MS
Rhamnus cathartica	MS	(-)	MS
Rhododendron ponticum	R	MR	MR
Rosa canina etc.	MR/MS	S	S
Rubus fruticosus	S	S	S
Rubus idaeus	S	S	MS/S
Salix caprea etc.	MR/MS	MS/S	MS/S
Sambucus nigra	MS	S	S
Sarothamnus scoparius	R	MR/MS	S
Sorbus aucuparia	MR/MS	S	MS
Ulex europaeus	R	R/MR	MR/MS
Ulex gallii and *minor*	R	MR	MS
Viburnum opulus	MS/MR	MR/MS	MR/MS

Notes: S   = susceptible   MR = moderately resistant
MS = moderately susceptible   R   = resistant
(-) = not tested

Stem treatments
These techniques are appropriate for winter application, or for woody growth so tall that the foliage cannot be effectively sprayed, and where the resulting dead standing stems can be accepted or conveniently removed. Costs are relatively high and the need for oil or paraffin as a diluent for 2,4,5-T is a disadvantage.

Cut stump treatment
This method is used for control of coppice regrowth after felling (of crop trees or scrub) and avoids the problem of unsightly dead stems remaining standing on the site. As with stem treatments, the cost per treated hectare is relatively high.

6.3 **FOLIAR TREATMENT**
6.3.1 **FOSAMINE AMMONIUM**
Approved product
48% w/v liquid: Krenite (Selectokil).

Description
A translocated herbicide which arrests bud growth (rather than killing stems or roots) on many deciduous broadleaved woody weed species. Activity is not noticeable until the year following treatment. Only deciduous broadleaved woody weeds are controlled: evergreen broadleaves such as gorse, broom and rhododendron are resistant. Brambles are suppressed or killed.

Toxicity
Fosamine ammonium has a very low mammalian toxicity and a very low toxicity to fish. On contact with the soil it is very quickly broken down.

Crop tolerance
All conifers except DF, WH and larch: will tolerate up to 10 litres per hectare after hardening off (July onwards).

DF, WH and larch: rather more sensitive, but during August will tolerate up to 5 litres per hectare with only slight damage. Higher rates at other times may cause serious damage.

Broadleaves: deciduous species are susceptible to directly applied sprays. Always use a guard or direct the spray to avoid the foliage of crop trees. Evergreen broadleaves are tolerant.

Rates and methods of application
Applied as 5.0 - 10.0 litres of product per hectare (2.4 - 4.8 kg ai/ha) diluted in water through the following applicators:

Overall application
(a) Knapsack sprayer at MV (200 - 300 l/ha).
(b) Knapsack sprayer with 'VLV' nozzle at LV (60 - 130 l/ha).
(c) Mistblower at LV (90 - 175 l/ha).
(d) Drenchgun for spot application at LV (30 - 60 l/ha).

Placed spray
(a) Knapsack sprayer (with guard if required) at MV (200 - 300 l/ha).
(b) Knapsack sprayer with 'VLV' nozzle (with guard if required) at LV (60 - 130 l/ha).

Fosamine ammonium is less effective if applied at very low or very high concentrations. Refer to Section 11 for details of applicators, nozzles, flow rates and correct calibration.

Date of application
July to September prior to leaf senescence.

6

Safety precautions

Wash hands before meals, before attending to personal needs and at the end of the day's work.

Read Section 9. In particular observe the standard precautions and working practice outlined in Section 9.3.

Ensure that operators and supervisors are trained in the necessary skills and have the relevant Forest Safety Guides.

The label on the herbicide container has been designed for your protection - ALWAYS READ THE INSTRUCTIONS ON THE LABEL.

Protective clothing

See table of Protective Clothing Required (Section 10) for the clothing appropriate to the method of application selected. Please note the special requirements when handling and mixing concentrates.

6

6.3.2 GLYPHOSATE

Approved product
36% w/v liquid: Roundup (Monsanto).

Description
A translocated herbicide taken up by the foliage and conveyed to the roots. It causes chlorosis and eventual death of leaves and inhibits growth of roots and shoots.

Glyphosate controls a wide range of weeds including most grasses and broadleaved herbs, bracken, heather, bramble and most woody weeds (main exceptions are gorse and broom: see Section 7). On the latter group there may be little effect until the following season when roots die and much resuckering is prevented.

Toxicity
Glyphosate has a low mammalian toxicity and is harmful to fish. On contact with the soil it is very quickly broken down. Planting can be carried out immediately after treatment.

Crop tolerance
SS, NS, SP, CP, LP, RC and LC: will tolerate overall sprays provided leader growth has hardened. Hardening can occur as early as the end of July or may be delayed until October in some locations and seasons. To avoid damage to lammas growth, herbicide sprays must be directed away from leaders. During the active growing season trees must be guarded or the spray placed to avoid contact with the crop.

DF: as above but rather more sensitive.

Broadleaves and larch: will not tolerate overall application; always use a guard or a placed spray to avoid contact with the crop.

Rates and methods of application
Applied as 2.0 - 3.0 litres of product per hectare (0.72 - 1.1 kg ae/ha) diluted in water. Susceptible species can be controlled at the 2-litre rate, whilst brambles generally require the 3-litre rate as do those species classed as moderately susceptible in Table II.

For pre-planting treatment, particularly of areas with dense weed growth or with moderately resistant species present, the rate should be increased to 5.0 litres of product per hectare (1.8 kg ae/ha) to ensure good control.

The following applicators may be used:

Overall application
(a)   Knapsack sprayer at MV (200 - 300 l/ha).
(b)   Knapsack sprayer with 'VLV' nozzle at LV (60 - 130 l/ha).
(c)   Mistblower at LV (90 - 175 l/ha). This method is more effective than ULV for taller denser foliage as the fan-assisted flow gives better penetration.
(d)   ULVA at VLV (15 - 30 l/ha). For full effect, dilute the herbicide with at least 5 times the volume of water.

(e)   Tractor mounted boom sprayer at MV (200 - 300 l/ha).
(f)   Tractor mounted Ulvaforest at VLV (10 - 20 l/ha).

Placed spray
(a)   Knapsack sprayer (with guard if required) at MV (200 - 300 l/ha) or with 'VLV' nozzle at LV (60 - 130 l/ha).
    Refer to Section 11 for details of applicators, nozzles, flow rates and correct calibration.

Date of application
June to August inclusive but after new growth on crop trees has hardened. Glyphosate works best when weeds are actively growing.

Limitations
1.   Diluted glyphosate may denature after 2 to 3 days. Where possible use tap water as the diluent and only mix sufficient for the day's programme.
2.   Glyphosate is most effective on moist vegetation when relative humidity and air temperatures are high.
3.   Heavy rainfall within 24 hours of application may reduce the herbicide's effectiveness by preventing sufficient foliar absorption.
4.   On woody weeds and mixtures, mistblowing is usually the most effective of the handheld methods but it is also likely to inflict a higher degree of damage on unhardened crop trees.

Safety precautions
Wash hands before meals, before attending to personal needs and at the end of the day's work.
    Read Section 9. In particular observe the standard precautions and working practice outlined in Section 9.3.
    Ensure that operators and supervisors are trained in the necessary skills and have the relevant Forest Safety Guides.
    The label on the herbicide container has been designed for your protection -ALWAYS READ THE INSTRUCTIONS ON THE LABEL.

Protective clothing
See table of Protective Clothing Required (Section 10) for the clothing appropriate to the method of application selected. Please note the special requirements when handling and mixing concentrates.

6.3.3 **2,4,5-T**
Approved products
Emulsifiable concentrate of a low-volatile ester:
Marks Brushwood Killer (Marks).

Description
2,4,5-T is a plant growth regulating herbicide to which most
broadleaves are susceptible. It is a translocated herbicide absorbed
mainly through the aerial parts of the plant but also through the
roots. The oil-soluble ester is usually formulated into an
emulsifiable concentrate which can be applied in mixture with
water, oil or paraffin.
Formulations containing low-volatile esters are preferable so as
to reduce the danger of volatilised 2,4,5-T drifting on to
neighbouring agricultural or forest crops.

Toxicity
2,4,5-T has a moderate mammalian toxicity and is harmful to fish.
Its activity in the soil is low although it may persist for up to 6
months before breaking down.
One month should elapse between treatment and subsequent
planting.

Crop tolerance
SS,NS,SP,CP,DF,GF and NF: will tolerate overall sprays after
shoot growth has ceased and resting buds have formed.
WH,RC and LC: rather more sensitive, but will tolerate the
lowest application rates from September/October up to 14 days
before spring flushing.
LP, Larches, RAP and PDP: susceptible to overall application
but can be treated if the crop trees are guarded or the spray very
carefully directed to avoid contact with the crop.
Broadleaves: damaged or killed at any time by overall spraying of
2,4,5-T. Broadleaved crops can be treated by careful placed
spraying but damage from volatilisation of 2,4,5-T during hot
weather restricts treatment to winter months.

Rates and methods of application
Applied as 4.5 - 7.0 litres of product per hectare (2.25 - 3.5 kg ae/ha)
diluted in water through the following applicators:

Overall application
(a) Knapsack sprayer at MV (200 - 300 l/ha).
(b) Mistblower at LV (90 -175 l/ha). This method is more
     effective than ULV for taller denser foliage as the fan-assisted
     flow gives better penetration.

Placed spray
(a) Knapsack sprayer (with guard if required) at MV (200 -
     300 l/ha).
Refer to Section 11 for details of applicators, nozzles, flow rates
and correct calibration.

6

Date of application

Mid-July to early autumn, after crop trees have ceased shoot growth and formed resting buds, and before the woody weed leaves show signs of senescence. Bramble and other evergreen woody weeds can be sprayed throughout the autumn and winter to within 14 days of the crop's spring flush.

Limitations

Special precautions are required in WATER CATCHMENT AREAS and in areas regularly visited by the public in significant numbers - see Section 9.4.

Safety precautions

SEE SECTION 9.5 for special precautions for operators using 2,4,5-T.

Wash hands before meals, before attending to personal needs and at the end of the day's work.

Read Section 9. In particular observe the standard precautions and working practice outlined in Section 9.3.

Ensure that operators and supervisors are trained in the necessary skills and have the relevant Forest Safety Guides.

The label on the herbicide container has been designed for your protection - ALWAYS READ THE INSTRUCTIONS ON THE LABEL.

Protective clothing

See table of Protective Clothing Required (Section 10) for the clothing appropriate to the method of application selected. Please note the special requirements when handling and mixing concentrates.

6

6.4 STEM TREATMENTS

6.4.1 AMMONIUM SULPHAMATE

Approved product

Soluble crystals: Amcide (Battle, Hayward & Bower).

Description

A highly soluble translocated, contact and soil-acting herbicide which is absorbed through leaves roots and exposed live tissue surfaces. It is effective against most woody species including some, such as rhododendron, hawthorn and ash, which are less susceptible to 2,4,5-T and 2,4-D. It is extremely corrosive of metals and alloys including copper, brass, mild steel and galvanised iron.

Toxicity

Ammonium sulphamate has a low mammalian toxicity and a low toxicity to fish. Breakdown in the soil can take up to 12 weeks during which time it retains its herbicidal properties. Three months should elapse between treatment and subsequent planting.

Crop tolerance

All crop species are severely damaged or killed by direct application of ammonium sulphamate or by soil-percolation to the roots.

Post-planting frill-girdling or notching can be done safely if great care is taken to avoid unnecessary spillage or overflow reaching the ground. Pre-planting treatment is preferable.

Rates and methods of application

Frill girdling

A frill is cut round each stem by overlapping downward strokes of a light axe or billhook and the exposed live tissue is sprayed to runoff with a 40% solution of ammonium sulphamate (0.4 kg crystals per litre of water) using a plastic watering can or a Tecnoma T16 semi-pressurised knapsack sprayer (see Section 11.1.3).

Notching

Individual notches are cut round the stem by single downward axe strokes penetrating the live cambial tissue. Notches should be at least 3 cm long and should not be further than 10 cm apart, edge to edge. 15 g of dry crystals are placed in each notch.

Date of application

On a dry day at any time of year.

Limitations

Ammonium sulphamate is corrosive and should only be applied through the recommended plastic applicators.

Safety precautions

Wash hands before meals, before attending to personal needs and at the end of the day's work.

Read Section 9. In particular observe the standard precautions and working practice outlined in Section 9.3.

Ensure that operators and supervisors are trained in the necessary skills and have the relevant Forest Safety Guides.

The label on the herbicide container has been designed for your protection - ALWAYS READ THE INSTRUCTIONS ON THE LABEL.

Protective clothing
See table of Protective Clothing Required (Section 10) for the clothing appropriate to the method of application selected. Please note the special requirements when handling and mixing concentrates.

6

6.4.2 **2,4-D AMINE**
Approved products
50% w/v liquid:

Farmon 2,4-D	(Farm Protection)
Marks 2,4-D-A	(Marks)
MSS 2,4-D Amine	(Mirfield Sales Services)
Palormone D	(Universal Crop Protection)

All are ACAS-approved products although not specifically named for forest use. As far as can be ascertained none of these products was included in the original trials of 2,4-D amine treatment but there is no reason to suppose that any one of them will prove ineffective.

Description
2,4-D is a plant growth regulating herbicide to which many broadleaves (herbaceous and woody) are susceptible. It is absorbed mainly through aerial parts of the plant but also through the roots. For stem injection of woody broadleaves the water-soluble amine translocates easily within the stem and is thus more effective than the less mobile ester.

Toxicity
2,4-D has a moderate mammalian toxicity and is harmful to fish. It is broken down in the soil within 30 days. One month should elapse between treatment and subsequent planting.

Crop tolerance
All species: provided care is taken to avoid unnecessary spray spillage of 2,4-D, no crop damage should occur with the stem injection method.

Rate and methods of application
Tree injection
Incisions are cut at 50-75 mm centres round the stem (a) at waist level using a Hypo Hatchet or (b) near the base of the stem using a Jim Gem tree injector. 1.0 ml of undiluted 50% w/v amine salt formulation is injected into each incision.

Date of application
At any time of year.

Limitations
Special precautions are required in WATER CATCHMENT AREAS to avoid water taint - see Section 9.4.

Safety precautions
SEE SECTION 9.5 for special precautions for operators using 2,4-D.
Wash hands before meals, before attending to personal needs and at the end of the day's work.
Read Section 9. In particular observe the standard precautions and working practice outlined in Section 9.3.

6

Ensure that operators and supervisors are trained in the necessary skills and have the relevant Forest Safety Guides.

The label on the herbicide container has been designed for your protection - ALWAYS READ THE INSTRUCTIONS ON THE LABEL.

Protective clothing

See table of Protective Clothing Required (Section 10) for the clothing appropriate to the method of application selected. Please note the special requirements when handling and mixing concentrates.

6

6.4.3 GLYPHOSATE

Approved product
36% w/v liquid: Roundup (Monsanto).

Description
A translocated herbicide normally applied to and taken up by the foliage but which is also effective as a stem injection treatment. It causes chlorosis and eventual death of leaves and inhibits growth of roots and shoots.

Stem injection with glyphosate controls all the major broadleaved woody weed species and is also highly effective in killing individual stems of SS and other conifers, e.g. in chemical thinning.

Toxicity
Glyphosate has a low mammalian toxicity and is harmful to fish. On contact with the soil it is very quickly broken down. Planting can be carried out immediately after treatment.

Crop tolerance
There is no evidence of translocation across root grafts to untreated trees ('flashback'). Unwanted stems can be safely treated by this method among any crop species.

For foliar crop tolerance see Section 6.3.2.

6

Rates and methods of application
For trees up to 15 cm diameter: cut a single notch on one side of the stem using a hand axe or slasher and apply 2 ml of a 50% solution of Roundup in water.

For larger trees a second cut on the opposite side of the stem may be needed, and 2 ml of the 50% solution should be applied to each cut.

Date of application
At any time of year except during sap flow in spring.

Limitations
Diluted glyphosate may denature after 2 to 3 days. Where possible use tap water as the diluent and only mix sufficient for the day's programme.

Safety precautions
Wash hands before meals, before attending to personal needs and at the end of the day's work.

Read Section 9. In particular observe the standard precautions and working practice outlined in Section 9.3.

Ensure that operators and supervisors are trained in the necessary skills and have the relevant Forest Safety Guides.

The label on the herbicide container has been designed for your protection - ALWAYS READ THE INSTRUCTIONS ON THE LABEL.

Protective clothing

See table of Protective Clothing Required (Section 10) for the clothing appropriate to the method of application selected. Please note the special requirements when handling and mixing concentrates.

6

6.4.4 **2,4,5-T**
Approved products
Emulsifiable concentrate of a low-volatile ester:
Marks Brushwood Killer (Marks).
Description
2,4,5-T is a plant growth regulating herbicide to which most broadleaves are susceptible. It is a translocated herbicide absorbed mainly through the aerial parts of the plant but also through the roots. The oil-soluble ester is usually formulated into an emulsifiable concentrate which can be applied in mixture with water, oil or paraffin. Formulations containing low-volatile esters are preferable so as to reduce the danger of volatilised 2,4,5-T drifting on to neighbouring agricultural or forest crops.

Toxicity
2,4,5-T has a moderate mammalian toxicity and is harmful to fish. Its activity in the soil is low although it may persist for up to 6 months before breaking down.

One month should elapse between treatment and subsequent planting.

Crop tolerance
SS,NS,SP,CP,DF,GF and NF: will tolerate overall sprays after shoot growth has ceased and resting buds have formed.

WH,RC and LC: rather more sensitive, but will tolerate the lowest application rates from September/October up to 14 days before spring flushing.

LP, Larches, RAP and PDP: susceptible to overall application but can be treated if the crop trees are guarded or the spray very carefully directed to avoid contact with the crop.

Broadleaves: damaged or killed at any time by overall spraying of 2,4,5-T. Broadleaved crops can be treated by careful placed spraying but damage from volatilisation of 2,4,5-T during hot weather restricts treatment to winter months.

Rates and methods of application
Basal bark spray: 3 - 5 litres of 50% w/v emulsifiable low-volatile ester per 100 litres of paraffin (1.5 to 2.5 kg ae/100 litres of paraffin). Apply with a knapsack sprayer and lance, spraying the whole circumference of the bottom 30 - 45 cm of each stem until saturated to the point of runoff.

Frill girdling
A frill is cut by downward strokes of a light axe or billhook around each stem and the exposed live tissue is sprayed to runoff using the same herbicide preparation as for basal bark spray.

Tree injection
Incisions are cut at 50-75 mm centres round the stem (a) at waist level using a Hypo Hatchet or (b) near the base of the stem using a

6

Jim Gem tree injector. 1.0 ml of undiluted 50% w/v emulsifiable low-volatile ester is injected into each incision.

Date of application
At any time of year but, for basal bark and frill-girdling methods, it is advisable to avoid the growing season of any conifer crop present.

Limitations
Special precautions are required in WATER CATCHMENT AREAS and in areas regularly visited by the public in significant numbers - see Section 9.4.

Safety precautions
SEE SECTION 9.5 for special precautions for operators using 2,4,5-T.

Wash hands before meals, before attending to personal needs and at the end of the day's work.

Read Section 9. In particular observe the standard precautions and working practice outlined in Section 9.3.

Ensure that operators and supervisors are trained in the necessary skills and have the relevant Forest Safety Guides.

The label on the herbicide container has been designed for your protection - ALWAYS READ THE INSTRUCTIONS ON THE LABEL.

Protective clothing
See table of Protective Clothing Required (Section 10) for the clothing appropriate to the method of application selected. Please note the special requirements when handling and mixing concentrates.

6

6.5 CUT STUMP TREATMENT
6.5.1 AMMONIUM SULPHAMATE
Approved product
Soluble crystals: Amcide (Battle, Hayward & Bower).

Description
A highly soluble translocated, contact and soil-acting herbicide which is absorbed through leaves roots and exposed live tissue surfaces. It is effective against most woody species including some, such as rhododendron, hawthorn and ash, which are less susceptible to 2,4,5-T and 2,4-D. It is extremely corrosive of metals and alloys including copper, brass, mild steel and galvanised iron.

Toxicity
Ammonium sulphamate has a low mammalian toxicity and a low toxicity to fish. Breakdown in the soil can take up to 12 weeks during which time it retains its herbicidal properties.

Three months should elapse between treatment and subsequent planting.

Crop tolerance
All crop species are severely damaged or killed by direct application of ammonium sulphamate or by direct or indirect root-poisoning by percolation of the herbicide into the soil from treated stems and stumps. Cut stump application of ammonium sulphamate should therefore be restricted to pre-planting.

Rates and methods of application
Apply to freshly cut stump surfaces and all remaining foliage, twigs, and bark
(a) a 40% solution of ammonium sulphamate (0.4 kg crystals per litre of water) to the point of runoff, using a plastic watering can or a Tecnoma T16P semi-pressurised knapsack sprayer (see Section 11.1.3), or
(b) dry crystals at the rate of 6 g per cm of stump diameter.

Date of application
On a dry day at any time of year.

Limitations
Ammonium sulphamate is corrosive and should only be applied through the recommended plastic applicators.

Safety precautions
Wash hands before meals and at the end of the day's work.

Read Section 9. In particular observe the standard precautions and working practice outlined in Section 9.3.

Ensure that operators and supervisors are trained in the necessary skills and have the relevant Forest Safety Guides.

The label on the herbicide container has been designed for your protection - ALWAYS READ THE INSTRUCTIONS ON THE LABEL.

6

Protective clothing

See table of Protective Clothing Required (Section 10) for the clothing appropriate to the method of application selected. Please note the special requirements when handling and mixing concentrates.

6

6.5.2 GLYPHOSATE
Approved product
36% w/v liquid: Roundup (Monsanto).

Description
A translocated herbicide normally applied to and taken up by the foliage but which is also effective when applied to freshly cut stumps. As a cut stump treatment it reduces or stops the production of new shoots and kills the root system of the stump.

Glyphosate controls all the major broadleaved woody weed species and is also highly effective in preventing regrowth from remaining live branches on the stumps of SS and other conifers, e.g. for respacement of natural regeneration.

Toxicity
Glyphosate has a low mammalian toxicity and is harmful to fish. On contact with the soil it is very quickly broken down. Planting can be carried out immediately after treatment.

Crop tolerance
There is no evidence of translocation across root grafts to untreated trees ('flashback'). Cut stumps can be safely treated by this method among any crop species provided none of the herbicide is allowed to fall on the crop foliage.

For foliar crop tolerance see Section 6.3.2.

Rate and method of application
A 20% solution of the product in water (to which a suitable red dye (e.g.from Hortichem Ltd.) has been added) is applied to the freshly cut surface of each stump using a paint brush, a knapsack sprayer fitted with a hollow cone nozzle or a clearing saw fitted with a suitable herbicide spray attachment.

Date of application
October to April before the spring sap flow.

Limitations
1. Diluted glyphosate may denature after 2 to 3 days. Where possible use tap water as the diluent and only mix sufficient for the day's programme.
2. Rainfall within 24 hours of application may reduce the herbicide's effectiveness by washing the herbicide off the stump.

Safety precautions
Wash hands before meals, before attending to personal needs and at the end of the day's work.

Read Section 9. In particular observe the standard precautions and working practice outlined in Sections 9.3.

Ensure that operators and supervisors are trained in the necessary skills and have the relevant Forest Safety Guides.

6

The label on the herbicide container has been designed for your protection - ALWAYS READ THE INSTRUCTIONS ON THE LABEL.

Protective clothing

See table of Protective Clothing Required (Section 10) for the clothing appropriate to the method of application selected. Please note the special requirements when handling and mixing concentrates.

6

6.5.3 **2,4,5-T**
Approved product Emulsifiable concentrate of a low-volatile ester: Marks Brushwood Killer (Marks).

Description
2,4,5-T is a plant growth regulating herbicide to which most broadleaves are susceptible. It is a translocated herbicide absorbed mainly through the aerial parts of the plant but also through the roots. The oil-soluble ester is usually formulated into an emulsifiable concentrate which can be applied in mixture with water, oil or paraffin.

Formulations containing low-volatile esters are preferable so as to reduce the danger of volatilised 2,4,5-T drifting on to neighbouring agricultural or forest crops.

Toxicity
2,4,5-T has a moderate mammalian toxicity and is harmful to fish. Its activity in the soil is low although it may persist for up to 6 months before breaking down.

One month should elapse between treatment and subsequent planting.

Crop tolerance
SS, NS, SP, CP, DF, GF and NF: will tolerate overall sprays after shoot growth has ceased and resting buds have formed.

WH, RC and LC: rather more sensitive, but will tolerate the lowest application rates from September/October up to 14 days before spring flushing.

LP, Larches, RAP and PDP: susceptible to overall application but can be treated if the crop trees are guarded or the spray very carefully directed to avoid contact with the crop.

Broadleaves: damaged or killed at any time by overall spraying of 2,4,5-T. Broadleaved crops can be treated by careful placed spraying but damage from volatilisation of 2,4,5-T during hot weather restricts treatment to winter months.

Rates and method of application
3-5 litres of 50% w/v emulsifiable low-volatile ester per 100 litres of paraffin (1.5 to 2.5 kg ae/100 litres of paraffin). Apply with a knapsack sprayer and lance, spraying the freshly cut stump surface and the surrounding bark until saturated to the point of runoff.

Date of application
At any time of year but October to March is preferable since it is advisable to avoid the growing season of any conifer crop present.

Do not spray when stumps are wet or frozen.

6

Limitations

Special precautions are required in WATER CATCHMENT AREAS and in areas regularly visited by the public in significant numbers - see Section 9.4.

Resistant species which produce coppice shoots may require a second treatment to achieve complete control.

Safety precautions

SEE SECTION 9.5 for special precautions for operators using 2,4,5-T.

Wash hands before meals, before attending to personal needs and at the end of the day's work.

Read Section 9. In particular observe the standard precautions and working practice outlined in Section 9.3.

Ensure that operators and supervisors are trained in the necessary skills and have the relevant Forest Safety Guides.

The label on the herbicide container has been designed for your protection - ALWAYS READ THE INSTRUCTIONS ON THE LABEL.

Protective clothing

See table of Protective Clothing Required (Section 10) for the clothing appropriate to the method of application selected. Please note the special requirements when handling and mixing concentrates.

6

7. GORSE AND BROOM

7.1 General

These two evergreen shrubs occur separately or together and locally may present a major weed problem.

Recommended herbicides are:

AMMONIUM SULPHAMATE.

2,4,5-T.

TRICLOPYR.

The rates and methods of treatment for ammonium sulphamate and 2,4,5-T are the same as for other woody weeds and details can be found in the appropriate sections of Section 6. Recommendations for triclopyr are set out in Section 7.2.

Both species are resistant to fosamine ammonium and moderately resistant to glyphosate at the recommended rate for woody weeds.

7

7.2 **TRICLOPYR**
Approved product
Emulsifiable concentrate
48% w/v: Garlon 4 (Chipmans).

Description
A plant growth regulating herbicide which is rapidly absorbed mainly through the foliage but also by roots and stems. It controls a wide range of weed species but hawthorn is relatively resistant and grasses are not affected except at the highest rates of application. Triclopyr is particularly effective as a foliar spray on gorse and broom.

Toxicity
Triclopyr has a low mammalian toxicity but is classed as dangerous to fish. It is a mild eye irritant. In the soil it is broken down by microbial action.

Planting, especially of susceptible species, should be deferred until at least 8 weeks after spraying.

Crop tolerance
Spruces: will tolerate overall sprays provided leader growth has hardened. Hardening can occur as early as the end of July or may be delayed until October in some locations and seasons. To avoid damage to lammas growth, herbicide sprays must be directed away from leaders. During the active growing season trees must be guarded or the spray placed to avoid contact with the crop.

Pines: rather more sensitive than spruces with occasional leader damage if sprayed overall.

Larch, other conifers and broadleaves: severely damaged by overall sprays while in leaf. Late September application will be tolerated if applied with great care to avoid the foliage of crop trees.

Rates and methods of application
Applied as 3 - 6 litres of Garlon 4 per treated hectare (1.44 - 2.88 kg ae/ha) in water through the following applicators:

Band application
(a)   Knapsack sprayer at MV (200 - 300 l/ha).
(b)   Knapsack sprayer with 'VLV' nozzle at LV (60 - 130 l/ha).
(c)   Tractor mounted boom sprayer at MV (200 - 300 l/ha).

Triclopyr must not be applied at VLV or ULV.

Spot application will rarely be appropriate among such aggressive weeds.

Refer to Section 11 for details of applicators, nozzles, flow rates and correct calibration.

Date of application
July to September once leaders have hardened off (see Crop Tolerance above).

Limitations

1. Triclopyr is not cleared by PSPS for application at VLV or ULV.
2. If applied during very hot weather some volatilisation may occur with consequent risk to sensitive crops downwind.
3. Rainfall within 2 hours of application may reduce the herbicide's effectiveness by preventing sufficient foliar absorption.

Safety precautions

Wash hands before meals, before attending to personal needs and at the end of the day's work.

Read Section 9. In particular observe the standard precautions and working practice outlined in Section 9.3.

Ensure that operators and supervisors are trained in the necessary skills and have the relevant Forest Safety Guides.

The label on the herbicide container has been designed for your protection - ALWAYS READ THE INSTRUCTIONS ON THE LABEL.

Protective clothing

See table of Protective Clothing Required (Section 10) for the clothing appropriate to the method of application selected. Please note the special requirements when handling and mixing concentrates.

WEAR A FACE SHIELD WHEN HANDLING AND APPLYING THIS HERBICIDE.

7

65

8. RHODODENDRON
8.1 General

The glossy evergreen leaves of rhododendron have a thick waxy cuticle which is comparatively resistant to the entry of herbicides. To achieve adequate control, application rates need to be higher than for most other woody weeds. Moreover in older bushes, translocation is very restricted and it is necessary to spray almost the whole of the leaf area and stem surfaces to achieve good control.

Rhododendron is to be found on acid sites, mainly in the wetter western half of the country, in all phases of colonisation from a light scatter of small seedlings, through a partial cover of bushes to an impenetrable thicket 2-5 m in height.

The early stages of encroachment are (subject to terrain) easily accessible for herbicide application but bushes more than 1.5 m high must be manually or mechanically cleared to allow the stumps and the more susceptible regrowth to be sprayed, preferably before the regrowth is 1 m tall.

Four herbicides are recommended:
AMMONIUM SULPHAMATE.
2,4,5-T.
GLYPHOSATE.
TRICLOPYR.

Each of these is applied either as a foliar spray or as a cut stump treatment, and frequently in a combination of both techniques where cut stumps and young regrowth exist together.

8

8.2 AMMONIUM SULPHAMATE

Approved product
Soluble crystals: Amcide (Battle, Hayward & Bower)

Description
A highly soluble translocated, contact and soil-acting herbicide which is absorbed through leaves roots and exposed live tissue surfaces. It is effective against most woody species including some, such as rhododendron, hawthorn and ash, which are less susceptible to 2,4,5-T and 2,4-D. It is extremely corrosive of metals and alloys including copper, brass, mild steel and galvanised iron.

Toxicity
Ammonium sulphamate has a low mammalian toxicity and a low toxicity to fish. Breakdown in the soil can take up to 12 weeks during which time it retains its herbicidal properties.

Three months should elapse between treatment and subsequent planting.

Crop tolerance
All crop species are severely damaged or killed by direct application of ammonium sulphamate or by direct or indirect root-poisoning by percolation of the herbicide into the soil from treated stems and stumps. Ammonium sulphamate should therefore only be used pre-planting.

Rate and method of application
Apply a 40% solution of ammonium sulphamate (0.4 kg crystals per litre of water) to all accessible surfaces including freshly cut stumps and all remaining bark, twigs and leaves

A non-ionic wetter should be added to the spray solution at 6 ml per litre of spray solution.

Use a plastic watering can or a Tecnoma T16P semi-pressurised knapsack sprayer (see Section 11.1.4).

Date of application
On a dry day at any time of year.

Limitations
Ammonium sulphamate is corrosive and should only be applied through the recommended plastic applicators.

Safety precautions
Wash hands before meals, before attending to personal needs and at the end of the day's work.

Read Section 9. In particular observe the standard precautions and working practice outlined in Section 9.3.

Ensure that operators and supervisors are trained in the necessary skills and have the relevant Forest Safety Guides.

8

The label on the herbicide container has been designed for your protection - ALWAYS READ THE INSTRUCTIONS ON THE LABEL.

Protective clothing

See table of Protective Clothing Required (Section 10) for the clothing appropriate to the method of application selected. Please note the special requirements when handling and mixing concentrates.

8

8.3 **GLYPHOSATE**
Approved product
36% w/v liquid: Roundup (Monsanto).

Description
A translocated herbicide taken up by the foliage and conveyed to the roots. It causes chlorosis and eventual death of leaves and inhibits growth of roots and shoots.

Glyphosate controls a wide range of weeds including grasses, broadleaved herbs, bracken, heather and woody weeds. On the latter group there may be little effect until the following season when roots are killed and much resuckering prevented.

Toxicity
Glyphosate has a low mammalian toxicity and is harmful to fish. On contact with the soil it is very quickly broken down. Planting can be carried out immediately after treatment.

Crop tolerance
At the rates of application needed to kill rhododendron all crop species are severely damaged by overall treatments of glyphosate. Ideally all rhododendron control should be carried out pre-planting but, if a crop is present, treatment is possible if the spray is very carefully directed to avoid contact with crop trees.

Rates and methods of application
1.   Applied as 10 litres of product per hectare (3.6 kg ae/ha) diluted in water through the following applicators:

Overall application
(a)   Knapsack sprayer at MV (200 - 300 l/ha) or with 'VLV' nozzle at LV (60 - 130 l/ha).
(b)   Mistblower at LV (90 - 175 l/ha). This method is very effective as the fan-assisted flow gives good penetration thus requiring fewer access racks.
(c)   Herbi or ULVA at VLV (30 - 40 l/ha). For full effect, dilute the herbicide with at least 3 times the volume of water.
(d)   Tractor mounted boom sprayer at MV (200 - 300 l/ha).
(e)   Tractor mounted Ulvaforest at VLV (30 - 40 l/ha).

Placed spray
(a)   Knapsack sprayer using 'VLV' nozzles (with guard if required) at LV (50 - 100 l/ha).

2.   Alternatively spray all the foliage to wetness with a 1% (1 litre of product in 100 litres water) solution using a knapsack sprayer or a mistblower as appropriate.

Refer to Section 11 for details of applicators, nozzles, flow rates and correct calibration.

Date of application
June to September.

8

Limitations

1.   Diluted glyphosate may denature after 2 to 3 days. Where possible use tap water as the diluent and only mix sufficient for the day's programme.
2.   Glyphosate is most effective on moist vegetation when relative humidity and air temperatures are high.
3.   Heavy rainfall within 24 hours of application may reduce the herbicide's effectiveness by preventing sufficient foliar absorption.

Safety precautions

Wash hands before meals, before attending to personal needs and at the end of the day's work.

Read Section 9. In particular observe the standard precautions and working practice outlined in Section 9.3.

Ensure that operators and supervisors are trained in the necessary skills and have the relevant Forest Safety Guides.

The label on the herbicide container has been designed for your protection - ALWAYS READ THE INSTRUCTIONS ON THE LABEL.

Protective clothing

See table of Protective Clothing Required (Section 10) for the clothing appropriate to the method of application selected. Please note the special requirements when handling and mixing concentrates.

8

8.4   **2,4,5-T**
Approved products
Emulsifiable concentrate of a low-volatile ester:
Marks Brushwood Killer (Marks).

Description
2,4,5-T is a plant growth regulating herbicide to which most broadleaves are susceptible. It is a translocated herbicide absorbed mainly through the aerial parts of the plant but also through the roots. The oil-soluble ester is usually formulated into an emulsifiable concentratewhich can be applied in mixture with water, oil or paraffin. Formulations containing low-volatile esters reduce the danger of volatilised 2,4,5-T drifting on to neighbouring agricultural or forest crops.

Toxicity
2,4,5-T has a moderate mammalian toxicity and is harmful to fish. Its activity in the soil is low although it may persist for up to 6 months before breaking down. One month should elapse between treatment and subsequent planting.

Crop tolerance
SS,NS,SP,CP,DF,GF and NF: will tolerate overall sprays after shoot growth has ceased and resting buds have formed.
    WH, RC and LC: rather more sensitive, but will tolerate the lowest application rates from September/October up to 14 days before spring flushing.
    LP, Larches, RAP and PDP: susceptible to overall application but can be treated if the crop trees are guarded or the spray very carefully directed to avoid contact with the crop.
    Broadleaves: damaged or killed at any time by overall spraying of 2,4,5-T. Broadleaved crops can be treated by careful placed spraying but damage from volatilisation of 2,4,5-T during hot weather restricts treatment to winter months.

Rate and method of application
4-5 litres of 50% w/v emulsifiable low-volatile ester per 100 litres of paraffin (2.0 to 2.5 kg ae/100 litres of paraffin). Apply with a knapsack sprayer and lance to all accessible surfaces including freshly cut stumps and all remaining bark, twigs and leaves.
    A second treatment may be necessary the following season to achieve complete control.

Date of application
Pre-planting: at any time of year.
    Post-planting and if sensitive crops adjoin the treated area: October to March.
    Do not spray when stumps and foliage are wet or frozen.

8

RHODODENDRON
(2,4,5—T)

Limitations
Special precautions are required in WATER CATCHMENT AREAS and in areas regularly visited by the public in significant numbers - see Section 9.4.

Safety precautions
SEE SECTION 9.4.2 for special precautions for operators using 2,4,5-T. Wash hands before meals, before attending to personal needs and at the end of the day's work.

8

8.5 **TRICLOPYR**
Approved product
Emulsifiable concentrate
48% w/v: Garlon 4 (Chipmans).

Description
A plant growth regulating herbicide which is rapidly absorbed mainly through the foliage but also by roots and stems. It controls a wide range of weed species but hawthorn is relatively resistant and grasses are not affected except at the highest rates of application. Triclopyr is particularly effective as a foliar spray on gorse and broom and also gives good control of rhododendron.

Toxicity
Triclopyr has a low mammalian toxicity but is classed as dangerous to fish. It is a mild eye irritant. In the soil it is broken down by microbial action.

Planting, especially of susceptible species, should be deferred until at least 8 weeks after spraying.

Crop tolerance
At the rates of application needed to kill rhododendron all crop species are likely to be damaged by overall treatments of triclopyr. Ideally all rhododendron control should be carried out pre-planting but, if a crop is present, treatment is possible if the spray is very carefully directed to avoid contact with crop trees.

Rates and methods of application
1. Applied as 4 - 8 litres of Garlon 4 per treated hectare (1.92 -3.84 kg ae/ha) in water through the following applicators:

 (a) Knapsack sprayer at MV (200 - 300 l/ha) or with 'VLV' nozzle at LV (60 - 130 l/ha).
 (b) Tractor mounted boom sprayer at MV (200 - 300 l/ha).

2. Alternatively, for taller denser rhododendron, spray to wetness (but not to runoff) using a 1% mixture of Garlon 4 in water through the following applicator:

 Knapsack sprayer at MV (200 - 300 l/ha) or with 'VLV' nozzle at LV (60 - 130 l/ha).

Triclopyr must not be applied at VLV or ULV.

Spot application will rarely be appropriate among such aggressive weeds.

Refer to Section 11 for details of applicators, nozzles, flow rates and correct calibration.

Date of application
June to September. The rate of Garlon 4 required should be increased as the season progresses.

8

Limitations
1. Triclopyr is not cleared by PSPS for application at VLV or ULV.
2. If applied during very hot weather some volatilisation may occur with consequent risk to sensitive crops downwind.
3. Rainfall within 2 hours of application may reduce the herbicide's effectiveness by preventing sufficient foliar absorption.

Safety precautions
Wash hands before meals, before attending to personal needs and at the end of the day's work.

Read Section 9. In particular observe the standard precautions and working practice outlined in Section 9.3.

Ensure that operators and supervisors are trained in the necessary skills and have the relevant Forest Safety Guides.

The label on the herbicide container has been designed for your protection - ALWAYS READ THE INSTRUCTIONS ON THE LABEL.

Protective clothing
See table of Protective Clothing Required (Section 10) for the clothing appropriate to the method of application selected. Please note the special requirements when handling and mixing concentrates.

WEAR A FACE SHIELD WHEN HANDLING AND APPLYING THIS HERBICIDE.

8

9. SAFETY PRECAUTIONS AND SAFE WORKING METHODS

9.1 TRAINING

The Forestry Commission's Education and Training Branch provides courses at three levels on working methods and equipment for application of herbicides:

(a) for Forest District Managers and District Foresters, a short technical update Chemical Weed Control Course of 1 - 2 days duration.

(b) for District Foresters and Foresters in charge of spraying operations, a full Chemical Weed Control Course of 4 days duration.

(c) in certain instances Education and Training Branch instructors will carry out training of industrial spraying teams.

It is the duty of District Foresters and Foresters in charge of spraying teams to ensure that operators are fully trained. Education and Training Branch will supply relevant training guides and advice if required.

For Forestry Commission staff, details of training courses can be found in the Training Handbook.

Private sector readers should arrange training through the Forestry Training Council, c/o Forestry Commission, 231 Corstorphine Road, Edinburgh, EH12 7AT. Telephone: 031-334-8083.

9.2 THE FORESTRY SAFETY COUNCIL AND FOREST SAFETY GUIDES

The Forestry Safety Council (FSC) has been set up to co-ordinate all aspects of safety and to improve and foster safe working practices in the forest industry.

As an aid to the training of operators, the FSC publishes a series of Safety Guides each of which gives advice on safety aspects of a particular forest operation. These Guides have no legal status as such but courts have recognised their authority in the past and they could be used to decide legal liability.

Forest Safety Guides currently available which are relevant to the application of herbicides are:

FSC 2. Ultra Low Volume Herbicide Spraying (rev. 4/81)

FSC 3. Application of Herbicides by Knapsack Spraying (rev. 4/81)

FSC 4. Application of Granular Herbicide (rev. 4/81)

FSC 34. First Aid (rev. 12/82)

Each Forest Safety Guide is accompanied by a Safety Check List intended for use by supervisors, safety representatives, etc.

Guides are obtainable from:
The Secretary
Forestry Safety Council
c/o Forestry Commission
231 Corstorphine Road   Edinburgh EH12 7AT

Both operator and supervisor should be provided with a copy of the relevant leaflet which they should read and fully understand before starting any of the operations covered by these titles.

9.3 **ROUTINE PRECAUTIONS**

It is essential that the following precautions are read carefully and followed explicitly whenever chemicals are to be used.

Storage

— A cool, dark, frost-free store is desirable for all chemicals. Ensure that the store is constructed and labelled in accordance with Health and Safety regulations and with the requirements of the local Fire Officer. (FC staff must refer to the requirements laid out in Silvicultural Memorandum 3, revised 1985.)
— Keep all herbicides under lock and key.
— Retain makers' labels and leaflets for reference.
— Clearly label all containers, including those containing unused diluted material.
— Isolate all herbicides from people and animals.
— Check periodically for leakage and spillage; dispose of faulty container.
— Never transfer herbicides to other containers, especially not to empty drink bottles.

Handling of concentrates

— Always follow the instructions on the container or makers' leaflet.
— Wear protective clothing prescribed in Section 10 or as recommended on the container label.
— Avoid all contact of the concentrate with the skin and eyes. If this occurs wash off IMMEDIATELY using copious quantities of water. Remove any contaminated clothing IMMEDIATELY if it has absorbed herbicide concentrate and wash affected areas of skin.

Mixing

— Calculate accurately the correct quantity of concentrate to add to the required volume of carrying liquid. Always add the concentrate to the carrying liquid: NEVER vice versa.
— For calculating concentrations see Section 11.5.
— Never mix herbicides where any spillage or run off can find its way into watercourses. Never allow puddles or pools of herbicide to form.

— All measuring and mixing vessels should be reserved solely for these purposes.
— Stir thoroughly until mixing is complete. Agitate regularly to avoid settling out of suspended material.

Application
— Select the correct equipment for delivering the herbicide as recommended (i.e. MV, LV, VLV or ULV). This must be functioning properly and be free from leaks and blockages. (See Section 11).
— Make sure that the area to be treated is clear of both the public and domestic animals.
— Inform well in advance all interested parties, such as local beekeepers, sporting tenants, neighbouring landowners, water authorities etc., of intention to spray .
— Avoid spray drift on to non-target areas.
— Wear the full protective clothing recommended in Section 10.2, Table III

After application
— Wash hands before smoking, eating, drinking and attending to personal needs.
— Remove protective clothing before eating and drinking.
— Before storing clean all protective clothing used. Respirator filters should be changed according to makers' instructions.
— Store protective clothing and personal equipment well away from possible contact with herbicide.
— Wash out spraying equipment soon after use, using large quantities of water. Do not contaminate watercourses.
— Dispose of empty containers and surplus materials correctly and safely. As there are legal requirements for this, refer to information given in Sections 2.6 and 9.6. Do not burn empty containers.

9

9.4 **USE OF HERBICIDES ON SURFACE WATER CATCHMENTS**
The contamination of water in general, and drinking water in particular, by herbicides is undesirable. Some catchments are especially vulnerable and the likelihood of problems can be established by discussions with the appropriate water undertakings. Two types of problem may be encountered. Firstly very small quantities of some herbicides can create severe taste and odour problems (taint) in drinking water and secondly gross pollution can occur as the result of accidental spillage.

The phenoxy herbicides such as 2,4-D and 2,4,5-T are the most likely to cause problems of taint. These substances can taint water at concentrations as low as 1 microgram per litre (0.001 parts per million) after normal water treatment. The conditions controlling the formation of taints from these compounds cannot always be predicted and so water authorities will require that levels do not exceed, even for a short period, a few micrograms per litre in water for potable supply. Concentrations above this can occur quite easily if care and common sense are not exercised.

The concentration of herbicides in wash-off, should it occur shortly after spraying, is likely to be very much above this limit. We have therefore to ensure that water from the sprayed area is sufficiently diluted by water from adjacent unsprayed areas so as not to give problem concentrations by the time the water reaches the point where it is drawn for human consumption. There are a number of factors applicable to all herbicides, which will influence the decision.

Site - On peaty soils, most of the water falling in a period of heavy rain is likely to run off. In free draining mineral soils, with loose surface texture, there will be very little run-off. Other soils will represent all stages between these extremes. The topography, such as the steepness of the site, will also be important.

Weather - The longer the interval between spraying and rainfall the more herbicide will be absorbed by the plants and soil and the less will be washed off. If rain follows closely after herbicide application, then in addition to run-off there will be loss of herbicidal efficacy.

Area of catchment - The actual water catchment may be a relatively small part of the forested area to be treated.

Dilution - Calculations of dilution are made to determine the concentration of herbicide that might be present at the abstraction point, and to relate this to general guidelines and to the limits for the herbicide in question (Fawell, 1984). It must be appreciated that dilution/dispersion in water is not instantaneous and that proximity to the abstraction point must be considered.

Herbicides should be kept at least 10 metres away from watercourses and streams and at least 20 metres from the edge of a reservoir. To avoid problems of taint neither 2,4-D nor 2,4,5-T should be sprayed if rain is expected within 24 hours of application. Contamination owing to excessive surface water run-off following heavy rain should be avoided by spraying only during settled weather when the soil is unsaturated.

If we wish to guard against the chance that the weather forecast will be wrong and that, contrary to expectation, heavy rain falls within 24 hours or so of spraying, then tainting with 2,4,-D or 2,4,5-T will be avoided if the area sprayed is restricted.

The following is a very simple example of the type of calculation which can form the basis of such restriction. Assume that the amount of herbicide washed off will be in proportion to the rainfall up to a maximum of one inch (25 mm of rain) but that 50% of the herbicide will be absorbed by plants and soil. Then the concentration of 2,4-D in water from areas sprayed at (for example) 5 kg per hectare will be roughly 10 parts per million. As 0.01 parts per million is the most water authorities will permit, then, where most of the rainfall is likely to run off, the area should not be more than 1,000th of the total catchment area.

If the water is taken from a reservoir then some further dilution will occur. In this case, the sprayed area may be increased, for example to 1/500th of the water catchment area feeding the reservoir.

If 2,4-D is being applied post-planting at 4 kg per hectare, the sprayed area should be no more than 1/800th or 1/400th of the catchment area respectively, and pro rata for other rates of application of 2,4-D.

Local water authorities (and River Purification Boards in Scotland) should be consulted if the use of herbicides is being considered in any surface water catchment area. In upland areas, they should be able to assist in determining the extent of water catchments. It may be more difficult to determine the precise location and area of catchments of small supplies for isolated farms and dwellings especially when they are private supplies.

Seal containers when not in use. To avoid any risk of pollution by back siphonage, do not connect any vessel containing herbicide direct to the public water supply. Hose pipes must not be put into containers when diluting herbicides or left unattended during filling. In the event of any incident inform the local water undertaking immediately.

9

9.5 PRECAUTIONS WHEN USING 2,4,5-T AND 2,4-D

9.5.1 Protection of operators

2,4-D and 2,4,5-T have a relatively low level of toxicity to man and animals but prolonged exposure, notably to oil solutions, may cause skin or eye irritation to some individuals. Recommended gloves and face shield should be worn by personnel mixing spray materials. Prolonged breathing of fine droplets of 2,4,5-T in oil can irritate the respiratory system. Face shields and filtering face piece respirators must be used by those applying 2,4,5-T in oil.

9.5.2 Protection of the public

If possible 2,4-D and 2,4,5-T should NOT be applied in those areas regularly visited by the public in significant numbers, and where blackberries, raspberries, mushrooms or other edible plants or fruits are likely to be exposed to spray. If, however, spraying does take place in any such area, appropriate notices must be erected during and for a short period after the operation.

9.5.3 **Protection of bees**
There is a risk to bees through ingestion when spraying heather in flower. This can be minimised by good liaison with local beekeepers.

9.6 **REFERENCES**
The following leaflets are available free of charge from MAFF (Publications), Lion House, Willowburn Estate, Alnwick, Northumberland NE66 2PF. (Tel. 0665-602881):

B 2078 *Guidelines for the use of herbicides on weeds in or near watercourses and lakes* (under revision, 1985).

B 2198 *Guidelines for the disposal of unwanted pesticides and containers on farms and holdings* (1980).

B 2272 *Guidelines for applying crop protection chemicals* (1983).

L 767 *Farm chemical stores* (1981).

L 792 *Controlled droplet application of agricultural chemicals* (1981).

— *Safe and effective spraying - a science not a gamble.*

Among the free leaflets published by the Health and Safety Executive, Banyards House, 1 Chepstow Place, London W2 4TF, the following relate to herbicides:

AS 6 *Crop spraying.*

AS 18 *Storage of pesticides on farms.*

The following paper may be obtained from the Water Research Centre (Environment), Medmenham Laboratory, Marlow, Bucks, SL7 2HD: Fawell, J K 1984. *The use of herbicides in forestry on potable water catchments.* WRC (Environment) Doc 549-M/1.

9

10. PROTECTIVE CLOTHING AND PERSONAL EQUIPMENT

10.1 General

The appropriate protective equipment, listed in Tables III and IV should be made available on a personal basis to all users of herbicides, including those handling herbicide containers.

All protective equipment should be kept clean and in good repair. Any damaged item should be properly repaired or replaced.

On completion of the spraying programme all equipment should be thoroughly cleaned and stored in a dry place away from direct sunlight, vermin and herbicides. Many herbicides have a distinctive and often unpleasant smell: some, if in contact with the skin for long periods, can cause dermatitis. For these reasons protective equipment should not be taken home. Care should be taken to ensure that the contaminated outside of the clothing does not come into contact with the clean inside.

Clothing should be washed at the forest stores or by a reputable cleaning firm in preference to taking contaminated garments into the home.

10

10.2 TABLE III   CLOTHING AND EQUIPMENT REQUIRED

Operation	Application equipment	Wellington boots	Gore-Tex suit Trousers	Jacket	Hood	Gloves	Face shield	Filtering facepiece respirator	Ear defenders	Note
Handling, mixing and filling (herbicides)	All types	E	E	E	E	E	E	E	-	(1)
Applying solid materials (granules, crystals, dusts)	1. Gravity/placement	E	E	D	D	E	D	D	-	(1)
	2. Motorised	E	E	D	D	E	E	E	E	(1)
Medium volume (MV) & Low volume (LV) spraying	1. Knapsack	E	E	E	E	E	D	D	-	(1) + (2)
	2. Drenchgun	E	E	E	E	E	D	D	-	(1), (2) + (4)
	3. Motorised mistblower	E	E	E	E	E	E	E	E	(1)
Controlled drop band (CDBA) or spot spraying (CDSA)	Herbi and Spot Herbi	E	E	D	D	E	D	D	-	(1)
Controlled drop incremental spraying (CDIA)	Ulva 8 Ulva 16	E	E	E	E	E	E	E	-	(1)
Direct application	Weedwiper mini	E	E	D	D	E	D	D	-	(1)
Spraying from tractor mounted equipment	MV, LV, CDBA and CDIA	E	E	E	E	E	E	E	E	(1), (2) + (3)
Tree injection	1. Hypo Hatchet	E	E	E	D	E	D	D	-	(1)
	2. Gim Gem	E	E	D	D	E	D	D	-	(1)

E = Essential; either advised under Pesticide Safety Precautions Scheme or considered necessary in relation to working conditions.

D = Discretionary: these items are not usually required but should be supplied on request to the operator or when noticeable exposure to a herbicide may arise through operations in unusual circumstances.

Recommendations for protective equipment requirements for use with application equipment not listed above should be obtained from Eastern Region Work Study Team (see back cover for address).

Notes: (1) Filtering facepiece respirators give adequate protection, particularly in combination with the faceshield. If the smell of herbicide is objectionable the 3Ms 8710 should be used. If operators object to the use of the filtering facepiece respirators, the Toxiguard RQ 2000 respirator should be issued.

(2) Face shield is essential when spraying paraquat, hexazinone or triclopyr.

(3) When operating tractors fitted with Q cabs, to which forced air ventilation units complete with an approved spray filter have been fitted, then none of the listed items need to be worn when spraying herbicides.

(4) For operator comfort, cotton glove liners should be worn during application.

10

10.3 **TABLE IV**
LIST OF RECOMMENDED PRODUCTS AND SUPPLIERS

EQUIPMENT	RECOMMENDATIONS	SUPPLIERS
Wellington boots	Dunlop Safety 8807 Nitrile/PVC Knee Boots Price £9.26 or Dunlop Safety 8808 as above with steel mid-sole Price £11.25	Greenham Tool Co. Ltd. 671 London Road Isleworth Middlesex TW7 4EX
Shoe chains	Rudd Shoe Chains Size 1: Shoe sizes under 5 Size 2: Shoe sizes 5-9 Size 3: Shoe sizes over 9 Price £7.75	Rudd Chains Ltd. 1-3 Belmont Road Whitstable Kent CT5 1QT
Spray suits (Trousers & jacket with hood)	Gore-Tex Suits PC48 available in small, medium & large sizes Price £69.50	FC supplier: Blairadam Clothing Store Clentry, Kelty, Fife, KY4 OJQ FC ONLY Private sector supplier: E McBean & Co Ltd, Woodilee Industrial Estate Kirkintilloch, Glasgow G36 3UZ
Gloves	Edmont Buna NX 37-175 Length 12″ sizes available 7 to 11. It is recommended that 2 pairs of gloves are issued to each operator. Price: depending on size £1.39 to £1.73 per pair	Arco Group Avon Mill Industrial Estate Mill Road Linlithgow Bridge Linlithgow West Lothian EH49 7QY
Cotton liner gloves (for use with the Drench gun)	Mens Cotton Stockinette Gloves, knitted wrist: Code 304111. Price £0.29	Greenham Tool Co. Ltd. 671 London Road Isleworth Middlesex TW7 4EX
Face shield	James North No.FS 1318 BW Price £5.61	Greenham Tool Co. Ltd. 671 London Road Isleworth Middlesex TW7 4EX

10

EQUIPMENT	RECOMMENDATIONS	SUPPLIERS
Face shield for use with safety helmet for tractor drivers	FC H417 aluminium frame for safety helmet. Price £7.71 FL8PC 8″ clear polycarbonate screen, wide flare. Price £4.96	Protector Safety Ltd. Great George Street Wigan Greater Manchester WN3 4DE
Filtering face-piece respirator. (Previously known as ori-nasal mask)	3 M's 8500 Non-Toxic Particle Mask, or 3 M's 8710 for odorous herbicides. Generally requires replacing after 2 hours use on a misty day or every 4 hours on a dry day. Price 8500 Box 50 £10.14 Price 8710 Box 20 £18.87	Herts Packaging Co. Ltd. 29 Mill Lane Welwyn Herts AL6 9EU
Respirators for protection against vapours and fine drops	Toxiguard Agricultural Respirator Type RQ 2000 fitted with 2 RC86 cartridges. Cartridges require changing every 8 hours. Price £8.93 Cartridges £1.86	Protector Safety Ltd. Great George Street Wigan Greater Manchester WN3 4DE

PERSONAL HYGIENE

Barrier cream	Rozalex Wet Guard available in 450 ml containers for personal issue. Price per case of 6 £14.43	Sterling Industrial Chapeltown Sheffield S30 4YH
Skin cleanser for use with water	Arrow Chemicals Tuffstuff available in 1 litre dispenser bottle. Price each £2.83 (also available in tubes and 5, 10 and 20 litre containers).	The Arrow Chemical Group of Companies PO Box 3 Stanhope Road Swadlincote Near Burton on Trent Staffs DE11 9BE
Skin cleanser for waterless use and for personal issue	Dekapol Handreiniger available in 100 ml tubes only.	Stockhausen Skin Protection PO Box 20 Scarborough North Yorks YO11 1DE

10

EQUIPMENT	RECOMMENDATIONS	SUPPLIERS
Liquid soap	Use Tuffstuff (as above) diluted 1:7 with water.	
Paper towels	Kimwipes Steel Blue 10″ rolls, Code 7148. In a case of 24 rolls Price per case £29.47 Minimum order 5 cases.	Kimberley Clark Ltd. Industrial Division Larkfield Kent ME20 7PS (Private sector: purchase locally from any industrial clothing supplier.)

Note: (1) This list is included as a guide to sources of supply and is **NOT** a comprehensive compilation of suppliers for recommended products. The omission of names of other possible suppliers does not imply that their services are unsatisfactory.

(2) 1985 prices are quoted only as an indication of likely costs. Current quotations should be sought by prospective purchasers.

10

10.4 **CLEANING RECOMMENDATIONS**
GORE-TEX SUITS
Grossly contaminated areas should immediately be rinsed well with water. Problems have arisen in connection with washing Gore-Tex spraying suits as some herbicides (notably Silvapron D) become slimy when mixed with soapy water. When this reaction occurs on the neoprene panels of the Gore-Tex trousers, the neoprene becomes swollen and tacky. To overcome this problem, the suit manufacturers have advised that the neoprene panels should be washed only with clear water, while the rest of the suit may be washed as usual, preferably with a pure soap powder. High pressure hoses should not be used to wash down the suits. Suits should be handled with care as rough treatment may cause blistering and reduce the liquid-repellent properties.

WELLINGTON BOOTS
Grossly contaminated areas should immediately be rinsed well with water. After work, the outside should be washed down with water and both inside and outside allowed to dry.

GLOVES
Grossly contaminated areas should immediately be rinsed well with water. At the end of each day the gloves should be washed inside and and out with soap/detergent and water, rinsed thoroughly with clean water, wiped dry inside and out, and allowed to dry thoroughly, avoiding extremes of heat and exposure to bright sunlight.

RESPIRATORS
It is important that respirators be cleaned each day with warm water plus a mild detergent, and sterilised with a solution of a disinfectant such as Dettol, TCP or Savlon.

10

11. EQUIPMENT

LIST OF CONTENTS

11

11.1 SPRAYERS FOR LIQUID HERBICIDES

11.1.1 Applications categorised by total volume applied

High volume spraying (HV) - Over 700 litres per hectare
Not recommended for herbicide application where high volume results in much waste and ground contamination due to run off. Better results with practically no run off can be obtained by using lower volumes per hectare.

Medium volume spraying (MV) - 200-700 litres per hectare
These rates give a good overall cover in most situations.
Equipment: boom sprayer, knapsack sprayer.

Low volume spraying (LV) - 50-200 litres per hectare
Good cover is achieved by the break-up of spray solution into fine droplets by means of an airblast or by a precisely engineered hydraulic nozzle. Equipment - Knapsack and tractor-mounted mistblower, knapsack sprayer fitted with 'VLV' nozzle.

Very low volume (VLV) - 10-50 litres per hectare
Controlled droplet band applicators (CDBA) or a drench gun spot applicator must be used at these very low applied volumes to obtain adequate cover and even droplet dispersal.
Equipment - Hand and tractor mounted rotary atomiser (300 micron) aerial application or drench gun.

Ultra low volume (ULV) - under 10 litres per hectare
CDBA or controlled droplet incremental applicators (CDIA) must be used to obtain adequate cover and droplet dispersal.
Equipment - Hand and tractor mounted rotary atomisers (30-300 micron).

MEDIUM VOLUME

11.1.2 Boom sprayers

As there is a wide range of sprayers available and as their use in the Forestry Commission is minimal, no specific recommendations are made here. Information and recommendations can be obtained from the Eastern Region Work Study Team (see back cover for address).

11

11.1.3 Semi-pressurised knapsack sprayer - Cooper Pegler CP15

The Cooper Pegler CP15 Forestry Model is the recommended knapsack sprayer for use in the Forestry Commission for the application of all herbicides except ammonium sulphamate (for which see details of the Tecnoma T16P below).

Supplier
Cooper Pegler & Co. Ltd.
Victoria Gardens
Burgess Hill
Sussex RH15 9LA
Telephone: 04 446 42526

Description

CP15 Forestry Model 15-litre Knapsack Sprayer, complete with pressure gauge and T-piece, pressure control valve and adaptor, straight extension lance and hose assembly. Ref. No. PA 1104 Price: £55.15

Accessories

Spray shield 30mm (12″) complete with Polijet (Green) Ref No. SA 04 630. Price £5.02.
Spray shield 35mm (15″) complete with Polijet (Green) Ref No. SA 04 631. Price £5.02.
Politec Tree Guard with two nozzles. Ref No. SA 04 637. Price £35.55.
Shoulder pads. Ref No. 03398. Price £3.98.
'VLV' nozzles complete with filters for band application.
Prices VLV 100 £2.75 VLV 200 £2.40

Output data

Nozzle type	Swathe width	Output at 1 bar (15 psi)
VLV 100	up to 1.8 m	7.6
VLV 200	up to 1.8 m	15.2

(ml/sec)

Polijet Nozzle Tip for band application Price £0.22.

| Nozzle type | Swathe width | Output in millilitres per second | |
		at 0.7 Bar (10 PSI)	at 1.0 Bar (15 PSI)
Red	up to 2.0m	33.3	41.2
Blue	up to 1.5m	22.5	27.2
Green	up to 1.0m	12.2	15.0

Note: The Green Polijet should be used only in conjunction with the spray shields.

The approximate application rates for the 'VLV' and Polijet nozzles held at a height to give a swathe width of 1.2 m with a walking speed of 60 m per minute and at a pressure of 1 bar (15 psi) are:

| VLV 100 | 65 l/ha. | Blue Polijet 200 l/ha. |
| VLV 200 | 125 l/ha. | Red Polijet 300 l/ha. |

Hollow Cone Nozzle Disc for Politec for spot application. Price: £0.17

89

Nozzle Cone Part No. 02-214 Disc Size Ref	Output in millilitres per second		
	at 0.3 bar (5 psi)	at 0.7 bar (10 psi)	at 1.0 bar (15 psi)
8	3.3	4.0	4.7
12	4.2	6.7	7.7
15	6.7	9.3	10.7
18	8.3	12.0	14.0
23	10.0	13.3	16.7

Tools required for maintenance and calibration

Pliers
Large screwdriver
Medium screwdriver
Adjustable spanner
Roll of PTFE plumber's tape
Plastic bucket

Large funnel
Metric graduated measure
Clean rags or absorbent paper
Watch
1-metre length of 6 mm diameter metal rod or dowel
50 m box tape

Calibration (See also Section 11.5.2B on calibration equations)

To calibrate the nozzle output:

1. Fill sprayer with water.
2. With sprayer on operators back, pressurise.
3. Set the pressure gauge by adjusting the screw of the pressure regulating valve to an initial pressure of 0.2 - 0.4 bar (4-6 psi) for the Politec or 0.7 bar (10 psi) for the Polijet.
4. Spray into the graduated measure for a set time.
5. Compare the actual nozzle output with the calculated output.
6. If there is a difference in the outputs, increase or decrease the pressure by adjusting the screw of the pressure regulating valve. Carry out items 4 and 5.
    Repeat until the actual and calculated nozzle outputs agree.
7. When outputs agree, note the pressure gauge reading for that sprayer.
8. The pressure noted in Item 7 should be checked two or three times per day using the same pressure gauge.
    Check the working height of the nozzle to obtain the correct swathe width.
    For spot treatment, check the duration of the burst required to give the correct applied volume for the area of the spot.

Droplet size

If undesirable drift is occurring use a larger droplet size by changing to a nozzle disc of the same type but with a larger hole and use at a lower pressure to obtain the same nozzle output. If necessary, adjust the working height of the nozzle to obtain the same width of treatment.

11

Cleaning
Wash thoroughly with a weak solution of detergent or soda and water. Shake well and spray out after removing the nozzle. Finally, pump through clean water.

Protective equipment
See Section 10 for requirements.

11.1.4 **Semi-pressurised sprayer** - Tecnoma T16P
The Tecnoma T16P is the knapsack sprayer recommended for use in the Forestry Commission only for the application of ammonium sulphamate. All the knapsack's working parts are plastic apart from two stainless steel ball bearings in the pump (which should not corrode)and a return spring in the trigger assembly (which will corrode and require replacing).

Supplier
J Mann and Son Ltd.
Saxham
Bury St. Edmunds
Suffolk IP28 6QZ

Description
T16P Tecnoma Knapsack Sprayer 17 litres fitted with an SKP 39017 adjustable nozzle. Price £50.00

Accessories
Weed killer shield Ref.No. KT 13050 Price £7.00

Tools required for maintenance
None are required as the sprayer can be dismantled by hand. Plastic bucket and clean rags or absorbent paper should be available.

Calibration
As the sprayer has no pressure controls and as ammonium sulphamate is applied to the point of runoff, no calibration is necessary.

Cleaning
Wash thoroughly with a weak solution of detergent or soda and water. Shake well and spray out after removing the nozzle. Finally pump through clean water several times.

Protective equipment
See Section 10 for requirements.

11.1.5 **Pressurised sprayers**
This type of sprayer is not recommended for general herbicide spraying.
Compared with the recommended semi-pressurised sprayer they are not as efficient, not as comfortable and require special safety precautions and checks.

11

LOW VOLUME

11.1.6 Semi-pressurised knapsack sprayer

The use of the CP15 knapsack sprayer fitted with 'VLV' nozzles (mentioned in Section 11.1.1) for low volume spraying at 50-200 l/ha is described in Section 11.1.3.

11.1.7 Knapsack mistblowers

The recommended sprayer is the Stihl SG17.

Supplier
Andreas Stihl Ltd.
Stihl House
Goldsworth Park
Woking, Surrey
Telephone: 04862 20222
Price £225

11.1.8 Tractor-mounted mistblowers

None is currently recommended.

VERY LOW AND ULTRA LOW VOLUMES
Controlled drop band applicators (CDBA)

11.1.9 Hand-held sprayer

The Micron Herbi 77 is the recommended sprayer for use in the Forestry Commission.

Supplier
Controlled Droplet Application Limited
Lockinge
Wantage
Oxfordshire OX12 8PH
Telephone: 0235 833314

Description
Micron Herbi 77 Price £43.50

11

Accessories required
Spare 2.5 litre plastic bottles, from CDA Ltd. Price £3.22
Spare motor or atomizer head (one spare per three sprayers) from CDA Ltd. Price of spare motor £14.00
Battery tester with voltage ranges of 0-1.5v and 0-12v.
Panda Multimeter, Model ELT 801, obtainable from local retailers or from:
Part International Ltd.
PO Box 50
Woodstone
Peterborough PE2 OJF
Price approximately £15.00

Eight batteries per sprayer. For small quantities, purchase locally. Large quantites from:
Varta Batteries Ltd.
Varta House
Gatwick Road
Crawley, West Sussex.
Telephone: 0293 547 631
Price (i) 2620 £0.40 each
       (ii) Alkaline 4014 (for larger programme) £0.85 each

Tools required for maintenance and calibration
Pliers
Screwdriver
Screwdriver No.2 Pozi 5332
Roll of adhesive tape
Plastic bucket
Large funnel
Metric graduated measure
Clean rags or absorbent paper
Watch
50m tape measure

Calibration (See also Section 11.5.2B on calibration equations)
To calibrate the nozzle output:
1.   Select the feed nozzle which suits the consistency of the diluted herbicide to be sprayed
      Blue nozzle: small diameter for slower flow
      Yellow nozzle: medium diameter
      Red nozzle: wide diameter for faster flow
      The ideal feed rate to the atomizer is 1 ml/s. At 2 ml/s and above atomization is not so efficient; small satellite droplets may form and present a drift hazard.
2.   Remove atomizer disc.
3.   Fill the plastic bottle with the mixture of herbicide to be sprayed and attach the bottle to the sprayer.
4.   Hold the sprayer at an angle of about 40 degrees. Before placing the nozzle over the graduated measure ensure that air bubbles are removed from the nozzle and feed pipe in order to obtain a constant flow. Measure the flow rate for a set time and divide to obtain ml/sec.
5.   If the flow rate is outside the ideal flow rate of 1-2 ml/s, change nozzle or adjust the angle at which the sprayer is held (10 degrees either way) until correct flow rate is obtained.
6.   Each sprayer must be calibrated as different flow rates can be obtained through similar coloured nozzles.
7.   Replace disc when calibration is complete.

11

Droplet size

Approximately 250 micron droplet with the atomizer disc revolving at 2000 rpm providing the voltage is between 4 and 12 volts. Check the voltage at the two electrical terminals on the outside of the atomizer head; if below 4 volts, replace batteries.

Cleaning

Wash thoroughly with a weak solution of detergent and rinse with clean water.

Remove batteries and clean off any corrosion on the contact points before storage.

Protective equipment

See Section 10 for requirements.

11.1.10 Tractor-mounted sprayer

The CDA Ltd. Ulvaforest is the sprayer being used and developed in the Forestry Commission. The sprayer has five Herbi atomizers (which can be used in any combination) fitted on to a 3.6 m gimballed folding boom, which is extendable by 0.56 m at each end. The tank capacity is 270 litres. The tank and boom assembly is fitted with a hydraulic ram which allows the boom to be raised to a height of 2 m.

The working technique for band application uses three atomizers. From CDA Ltd. Price on application.

Spot applicators

11.1.11 Drench gun

The Herbicator is the recommended drench gun for use in the Forestry Commission.

Supplier
Selectokil
Abbey Gate Place
Tovil
Maidstone
Kent ME15 0PP
Telephone: 0622 55471

Description
Herbicator Drench gun sprayer. Price £85.00 Spare knapsacks Price £7.00

Accessories
25-litre rigid polythene bottle with 18 mm tap bore. Ref BA/PS4. Price £11.35.

Supplier
Fisons Scientific Equipment Division
Bishop Meadow Road
Loughborough
Leics LE11 0RG

Tools required for maintenance and calibration
Pliers
Two 25 mm adjustable wrenches
Funnel
Plastic bucket
Metric graduated measure
Clean rags or absorbent paper
Tape measure
Castrol Girling rubber grease
Roll of PTFE plumber's tape

Calibration
1. Adjust gun to deliver a 5 ml dose.
2. Fill knapsack with 5 litres of water and mark this level (filler cap uppermost).
3. Prime gun.
4. With nozzle held at spray height over a dry surface, squeeze the trigger a number of times until a measurable spot appears. Measure spot diameter and calculate spot area (Table VII, page 106).
5. Calculate quantity of undiluted herbicide per spot/dose using calibration equation 6 of Section 11.5.2B.
   For example: glyphosate to be applied as Roundup at 1.5 litres per treated hectare.
   Spot area = 1.33 sq m
   $$\text{Volume per spot (ml)} = \frac{1.5 \text{ (litres)} \times 1.33}{10}$$
   = 0.1995 ml (say 0.2 ml).
   Therefore a 5 ml dose requires 0.2 ml of Roundup plus 4.8 ml of water. For a 5 litre knapsack these figures are multiplied by 1000.
6. Fill knapsack with herbicide and water accordingly.
7. Check the spot diameter as in 4. above.

Cleaning
Wash thoroughly with a weak solution of detergent or soda and water. Shake well and spray out, rinse by pumping through clean water. Once a week, or more frequently if necessary, split the gun by undoing the handle cramp screw, remove the complete cylinder assembly and apply a liberal quantity of oil to the moving parts.

11

Controlled drop incremental applicators (CDIA) for inter-row and overall application

11.1.12 **Hand-held sprayer**
The sprayers recommended are the Micron ULVA 8 and ULVA 16. The differences between these sprayers are:
   (i) The Ulva 8 is longer, allowing crops of up to an average height of 1.5m to be incrementally sprayed. It takes eight batteries.

(ii) The Ulva 16 is used for (a) inter-row spraying and (b) incremental spraying if the crop is not more than 1 m tall. It takes 16 batteries.

Supplier
Controlled Droplet Application Ltd.
Lockinge
Wantage
Oxfordshire OX12 8PH
Telephone: 0235 833314

Description
Micron ULVA 8   Price £33.00
Micron ULVA 16   Price £28.50

Accessories required
Spare 1 litre plastic bottles from CDA Ltd.
Price £1.35.
   Vibrotac high range rev. counter (one per gang) from CDA Ltd.
Price £12.50.
   Spare motor or atomizer head (one spare per three sprayers (from CDA Ltd. Price £7.50.
   8 or 16 batteries per sprayer. Alkaline batteries are recommended. If these batteries are used for 4 hours and then rested for about 20 hours before being used again they will give 25-30 hours total spraying time. For large quantities, obtain batteries type Alkaline 4014, price £0.85, from:

Varta Batteries Ltd.
Varta House
Gatwick Road
Crawley, West Sussex.
Telephone: 0293 547 631

   For larger programmes, rechargeable Cadmium Nickel batteries can be used. However, approximately 80 spraying days are required to break even in cost with Alkaline Manganese batteries. Obtainable through CDA Ltd. Price upon application.
   Dwyer Wind Meter from CDA Ltd.

Smoke powder from:
Brocks Fireworks Ltd.
Galeside
Sanquhar
Dumfries
Telephone: 06592 531

Price £13.54 for 10 tins each containing 125 g.
Spare nozzles from CDA Ltd. Price £1.50

11

Tools required for maintenance and calibration
Pliers
Screwdrivers 2½″ and 3″
Screwdriver No.2 Pozi 5332
Small adjustable wrench
Roll of adhesive tape
Plastic bucket
Large funnel
Metric graduated measure
Clean rags or absorbent paper
Watch
50 m tape measure

Calibration (See also Section 11.5.2B on calibration equations)
To calibrate the nozzle output
1. Fit required feed nozzle.

Nozzle colour	Nominal flow rate (water) (Note: thicker liquids flow more slowly)
Yellow	0.5 ml/s
Red	1 ml/s
Grey	2 ml/s
Green	3 ml/s

2. Fill the plastic bottle with the mixture of herbicide to be sprayed and attach the bottle to the sprayer.
3. Before placing the nozzle over the graduated measure, ensure that air bubbles are removed from the nozzle in order to obtain a constant flow. Measure the flow rate for a set time and divide to obtain the required ml/sec.
4. If necessary change nozzle and re-calibrate.
5. Each sprayer must be calibrated since different flow rates can be obtained through similar nozzles.
6. If during the day the temperature changes, the sprayer must be re-calibrated. A 5°C change will alter application rates by 12-15%.

Droplet size   Approximately 70 microns.
Droplet size is dependant on disc speed which should be checked with the Sirometer. 5500-8000 RPM is suitable for spraying, if below 5500 RPM, the batteries should be changed.

Wind speed
Wind speed should always be measured at the height of the sprayer.
For incremental spraying over an approximate 5 m swathe, a minimal speed of 3 kph (2 mph) is acceptable with a maximum speed of 12 kph (7 mph), occasionally gusting to 16 kph (10 mph).
For inter-row spraying of heather 0-19 kph (0-12 mph) is suitable.

11

Wind direction
Incremental spraying can be carried out if the angle between the operator's line of walking and the wind direction is not less than 20 degrees.

For inter-row spraying the wind direction is not as critical but it is better when blowing at 90 degrees to the operator's line of travel.

Safety zone
A 100 m safety zone, downwind, should be allowed where there are susceptible crops, especially those on adjoining farmland.

Cleaning
Wash thoroughly with a weak solution of detergent and rinse with clean water.

Remove batteries and clean off any corrosion on the contact points before storage.

Protective equipment
See Section 10 for requirements.

11.1.13 **Tractor-mounted sprayer**
The CDA Ltd. Ulvaforest is the sprayer being used and developed in the Forestry Commission. The sprayer has five Herbi atomizers (which can be used in any combination) fitted on to a 3.6 m gimballed folding boom which is extendable by 0.56 m at each end. The tank capacity is 270 litres. The tank and boom assembly is fitted with a hydraulic ram which allows the boom to be raised to a height of 2 m.

The working technique for overall application requires four atomizers. From CDA Ltd. Price on application.

11.2 **TREE INJECTORS**
The recommended tree injectors are the Jim Gem and Hypo Hatchet.
(a) The Jim Gem is basically a 1.2 metre metal tube which holds the the herbicide, with a chisel bit fitted to one end. A lever operates the pump which can be adjusted to deliver between 0.5 and 2.0 ml through the chisel into the cut. Price approximately £190.00.
(b) The Hypo Hatchet consists of a small hatchet which is bored to allow herbicide to be fed from a reservoir strapped around the operator's waist. When the hatchet hits the tree, a 1 ml dose of herbicide is injected. Price approximately £215.00.

Supplier
Stanton Hope Limited
422 Westborough Road
Westcliff on Sea
Essex SS0 9TL

11

11.3 DIRECT APPLICATORS FOR LIQUID HERBICIDES

These are applicators in which transfer of herbicide is effected by direct contact of a distributor (often a saturated wick) with the weed.

11.3.1 Hand-held direct applicator

The recommended applicator in the Forestry Commission is the Hortichem Ltd. Weedwiper Mini single head model.

Supplier
Hortichem Ltd.
14 Edison Road
Churchfield Industrial Estate
Salisbury
Wilts
Telephone: 0722 20133

Description
SM90 Weedwiper Mini Standard Single-head (Nylon wick) fitted with venting cap. Price £13.46.
SMR90 Weedwiper Mini Red Band Single-head (All-line wick) fitted with venting cap. Price £14.00.
The SM90 fitted with the nylon wick is recommended for use on normal vegetation. Where the vegetation is dense or semi-resistant, the faster-flowing SMR90 with the all-line wick should be used.

Accessories
Spare nylon or all-line wicks from Hortichem Ltd. Price £1.00 approx.
10 x 55g sachets of red dye from Hortichem Ltd. Price £6.90.
5 litre graduated polythene bottle with screw cap, tap and metal carrying handle. Ref PO 23/01. Price £5.05.
10 litre bottle as above. Ref PO 23/02. Price £6.45. Graduated bottles supplied by:
Fisons Scientific Equipment Division
Bishop Meadow Road
Loughborough
Leics LE11 ORG

11

Tools required for maintenance and calibration
Small adjustable wrench
Small funnel to fit filler cap
Metric graduated measure
Clean rags or absorbent paper
Plastic bucket
Teaspoon
Scrubbing brush
Plastic bags

Flow adjustment
1. Mark the reservoir (handle) at 75 cm from the filler cap. Always keep the level of herbicide above this point during use to ensure adequate wick flow.
2. Fill applicator with herbicide mixture to which has been added 1 teaspoonful of red dye per litre.
3. Open venting cap.
4. Allow wick to become impregnated with herbicide mixture. When fully impregnated the wick should be red.
5. Start treating the vegetation (see Working Method).
6. If the wick blanches during use, the compression nuts should be released to increase wick flow. It may also be necessary to pull the rubber seal from its seat and readjust its position on the wick.
7. If the wick remains bright red and drips during use, tighten the compression nut to reduce wick flow.

Working method
A back and forth sweeping action, taking care not to touch the crop tree, will ensure that both sides of the weeds are treated. Where the trees are standing above the weeds, application should be made in a triangular pattern. A double width pass will give control over a 0.8 m diameter spot (0.5 sq m). For trees below weed level, four back and forth passes over the tree, ensuring there is a 10 cm clearance between the wick and the top of the tree, will give control over 0.65 sq m.

Cleaning
In order to achieve maximum transfer of herbicide on to the weeds, any dirt adhering to the wick should be scrubbed off immediately. It is also recommended that during use the applicator head be immersed in water at intervals, or the applicator filled with water and left soaking overnight to cleanse the wick.

During use wicks should be replaced regularly. New wicks should be fitted after storage or if the old wicks have dried out.

Wash thoroughly with a weak solution of detergent and rinse with clean water.

Protective equipment
See Section 10 for requirements.

11.4 **GRANULE APPLICATORS**
It is recommended that gravity applicators be used in preference to motorised applicators as the former are more efficient and more comfortable to the operator.

There are two recommended types of gravity applicator:

11.4.1 (a) **Pepperpots**
These are supplied free with Atlas Lignum and propyzamide granules.

11

Accessories
A belt to hold 13 propyzamide beaker-type pots can be obtained from:
Kingswood Canvas Ltd.
197 Two Mile Hill Road
Kingswood
Bristol BS15 1AZ
Price £5.67.
A haversack to hold the Atlas Lignum pepperpots should be purchased locally.
For transportation the lids of the pepperpots should be sealed with an adhesive tape. Exchange the sealed lid for an unsealed one for application.

(b)   **Moderne applicator**
Use without the dose rate regulator fitted.
Supplier
Stewart and Co.
Stronghold Works
Mayfield Industrial Estate
Dalkeith
Midlothian EH22 4BZ
Price £5.90.

Application technique
For both the pepperpots and the Moderne, the technique is to shake the applicator from side to side whilst traversing the spot.

Calibration (See also Section 11.5.2B on calibration equations)
1.   Fill pepperpot or Moderne with granules.
2.   Using the side to side application technique shake the applicator for say 10 times over a paper or plastic sheet, measure the spot area and weigh the granules applied.
3.   Calculate that the amount applied is correct for the area treated.
4.   If not correct, adjust the vigour and number of passes of the application.

Protection equipment
See Section 10 for requirements.

11.5   **DILUTION AND CALIBRATION**
11.5.1 **Procedure**
Having selected the appropriate herbicide, application rate and pattern applicator and the overall quantity of material to be applied per hectare:

11

1. Calculate the likely equipment requirements and settings, choosing values for the relevant variables, e.g. for the knapsack sprayer:
    Nozzle size
    Spray pressure
    Dilution
    to give a convenient walking (or tractor) speed for the operator.
2. Calibrate the equipment on a small test area by setting up as calculated above and check the resulting application rate.
3. Adjust the variables to achieve the correct application rate.

11.5.2 Equations for calibration

A. Information required

The following parameters are required to solve the calibration equations:

(a) Walking or tractor speed, in metres per minute, from a timed run in the area to be weeded.
    Table VIII gives the conversion of seconds per 100 m to metres per minute.
(b) Nozzle flow rate, in millilitres per second from calibration.
(c) Volume rate in litres per hectare. Total quantity of herbicide and diluent.
(d) Swathe width or spot diameter.

The abbreviation ha in the equations refers to a treated hectare. A treated hectare is defined as the area within the plantation being weeded which is actually covered with herbicide.

B. Calibration equations

Table V indicates which of the following equations are applicable to the different types of applicators.

1. Nozzle output = $\dfrac{\text{Walking speed} \times \text{Volume rate} \times \text{Swathe width}}{600}$

   (ml/sec)   (metres/min)   (litres/ha)   (metres)

2. Walking speed = $\dfrac{\text{Nozzle output} \times 600}{\text{Volume rate} \times \text{Swathe width}}$

   (metres/min)   (ml/sec)

   (litres/ha)   (metres)

3. Volume rate = $\dfrac{\text{Nozzle output} \times 600}{\text{Walking speed} \times \text{Swathe width}}$

   (litres/ha)   (ml/sec)

   (metres/min)   (metres)

11

DILUTION AND CALIBRATION

4. Distance covered = Total volume of sprayer x 10,000
(metres)   (litres)
$$\frac{}{\text{Volume rate} \quad x \quad \text{Swathe width}}$$
Volume rate   x   Swathe width
(litres/ha)   (metres)

5. Volume of herbicide = Area of plantation x Volume rate x Swathe width
(litres)   (ha)   (litres/ha)   (metres)
Row spacing
(metres)

The fraction swathe width is presented in ready reckoner form in
row spacing   Table VI.

6. Volume per spot = Volume rate x Area of spot
(millilitres)   (litres/ha)   (m²)
10
Table VII gives spot area for given diameters.

7. Volume of herbicide = Volume per spot x Number of trees
(litres)   (millilitres)   (spots)
1,000
Table VII gives the number of trees per hectare for a given square spacing.

8. Number of trees sprayed = Volume of liquid in sprayer
(litres)
Volume per tree (litres)

9. Distance covered = Volume of liquid x 10,000 x Tree spacing
(metres)   in sprayer   in row
(litres)   (metres)
Volume rate   x   Area of spot
(litres/ha)   (m²)

10. Quantity of herbicide required per applicator/container =
(litres)
Applicator/container capacity x Herbicide rate
(litres)   (litres/ha)
Volume rate
(litres/ha)

11

EXAMPLE:
You require to know the walking speed at which to apply glyphosate
in a band with a Herbi at 1.5 litres of 36% W/V per ha, with 10 litres
per ha of fresh water diluent, giving a volume rate of 11.5 litres per
ha. The swathe width, measured, is 1.8 metres and the calibrated
nozzle output gives 1.5 ml/sec.

From Table V the walking speed for a Herbi refers you to
equation No.2.

Therefore: Walking speed = $\dfrac{1.5 \times 600}{11.5 \times 1.8}$ = 43.5 metres/min

103

TABLE V

CALIBRATION EQUATION APPLICABLE TO THE RECOMMENDED SPRAYER

To be calculated	Cooper Pegler CP15	Mistblowers	Herbi	Ulvaforest	Drench gun	Ulva 16/8	Granule* applicator
				SPRAYERS			
Nozzle output (litres/min)	1	1	1	1		1	
Walking/tractor speed (metres/ha)	2	2	2	2		2	
Volume rates (litres/ha)	3	3	3	3		3	
Distance covered (metres)	4/9	4	4	4	9	4	9
Volume of herbicide (litres)	5/10	5/10	5/10	5/10	7/10	5/10	7
Volume per spot (millilitres)					6		6
Number of trees sprayed					8		8

*Note: In the calculation, change litre/ml to kg/gramme for granular applicators

104

TABLE VI

AREA OF PLANTATION TREATED (1 ha)
BAND WIDTH x ROW SPACING

Width of band sprayed	Row spacing (metres)												
	1.5	1.6	1.7	1.8	1.9	2.0	2.1	2.2	2.3	2.4	2.5	2.6	2.7
2.4										1.00	.96	.92	.89
2.3									1.00	.96	.92	.88	.85
2.2								1.00	.96	.92	.88	.85	.81
2.1							1.00	.95	.91	.88	.84	.81	.78
2.0						1.00	.95	.91	.87	.83	.80	.77	.74
1.9					1.00	.95	.90	.86	.83	.79	.76	.73	.70
1.8				1.00	.95	.90	.86	.82	.78	.75	.72	.69	.67
1.7			1.00	.94	.89	.85	.81	.77	.74	.71	.68	.65	.63
1.6		1.00	.94	.89	.84	.80	.76	.73	.70	.67	.64	.62	.59
1.5	1.00	.94	.88	.83	.79	.75	.71	.68	.65	.63	.60	.58	.56
1.4	.93	.88	.82	.78	.74	.70	.67	.64	.61	.58	.56	.54	.52
1.3	.87	.81	.76	.72	.68	.65	.62	.59	.57	.54	.52	.50	.48
1.2	.80	.75	.71	.67	.63	.60	.57	.55	.52	.50	.48	.46	.44

11

TABLE VII

AREA OF PLANTATION TREATED (1 ha)
SPOT APPLICATION

Spot diameter (m²)	Spot area (m²)	Tree spacing (m)												
		1.5	1.6	1.7	1.8	1.9	2.0	2.1	2.2	2.3	2.4	2.5	2.6	2.7
2.4	4.52											.72	.67	.62
2.3	4.15										.72	.66	.61	.57
2.2	3.80									.72	.66	.61	.56	.52
2.1	3.46								.71	.65	.60	.55	.51	.47
2.0	3.14							.71	.65	.59	.55	.50	.46	.43
1.9	2.84						.71	.64	.59	.54	.49	.45	.42	.39
1.8	2.54					.70	.64	.58	.52	.48	.44	.41	.38	.35
1.7	2.27				.70	.63	.57	.51	.47	.43	.39	.36	.34	.31
1.6	2.01			.70	.62	.56	.50	.46	.42	.38	.35	.32	.30	.28
1.5	1.77		.69	.61	.55	.49	.44	.40	.37	.33	.31	.28	.26	.24
1.4	1.54	.68	.60	.53	.48	.43	.39	.35	.32	.29	.27	.25	.23	.21
1.3	1.33	.59	.52	.46	.41	.37	.33	.30	.27	.25	.23	.21	.20	.18
1.2	1.13	.50	.44	.39	.35	.31	.28	.26	.23	.21	.20	.18	.17	.16
1.1	.95	.42	.37	.33	.29	.26	.24	.22	.20	.18	.16	.15	.14	.13
1.0	.79	.35	.31	.27	.24	.22	.20	.18	.16	.15	.14	.13	.12	.11
0.9	.64	.28	.25	.22	.20	.18	.16	.15	.13	.12	.11	.10	.09	.09
0.8	.50	.22	.20	.17	.15	.14	.13	.11	.10	.09	.09	.08	.07	.07
0.7	.38	.17	.15	.13	.12	.11	.10	.09	.08	.07	.07	.06	.06	.05
0.6	.28	.12	.11	.10	.09	.08	.07	.06	.06	.05	.05	.04	.04	.04
0.5	.20	.09	.08	.07	.06	.06	.05	.05	.04	.04	.03	.03	.03	.03
Number of trees/ha (Assuming square spacing)		4444	3906	3460	3086	2770	2500	2267	2066	1890	1736	1600	1479	1371

11

TABLE VIII
WALKING OR TRACTOR SPEED IN METRES/MINUTE
FROM A TIMED 100 m RUN

Time (Sec/100 m)	Metres/minute
360	17
288	21
240	25
206	29
180	33
160	38
144	42
131	46
120	50
90	67
72	83
60	100
51	117
45	133
40	150
36	167

$$[\text{Based on m/minute} = \frac{100 \text{ m} \times 60 \text{ seconds}}{\text{Time (sec/100 m)}} \text{ and rounded up}]$$

11.6 STANDARD TIME TABLES AND OUTPUT GUIDES

The following output guides are current and available from Chief Work Study Officer, Forestry Commission, 231 Corstorphine Road, Edinburgh EH12 7AT.

XV/G5	(1972)	Spot spraying using knapsack sprayers
XV/G7	(1972)	Spraying herbicides with knapsack mist-blower
XV/G8	(1973)	Cut stump and basal bark treatment with 100% 2,4,5-T in oil using knapsack sprayer or live reel sprayer.
XV/G9	(1973)	Tree injection using a Swedish water pistol and Boy Scout axe
XV/G11	(1974)	ULV application of herbicides
XV/G12	(1977)	Tractor-mounted controlled droplet application
XV/G14	(1981)	Herbi CDA - band application - output guide
XV/G15	(1984)	Spot spraying using the Drench gun
XV/G16	(1984)	Spot application using the Weedwiper

The following output guides are no longer current and are out of print. Many managers may still possess a copy and will find their contents useful as background guidance. Before planning any major programme, however, managers should consult the nearest FC Work Study Branch for up-to-date advice.

11

XV/G2	(1971)	Foliar spraying with the Victair tractor-mounted mistblower
XV/G3	(1972)	Applying atrazine using a knapsack sprayer
XV/G4	(1971)	The application of chlorthiamid (Prefix)
XV/G6	(1972)	Foliage spraying with 50% 2,4,5-T in water using knapsack sprayers

11.7 CALCULATING COSTS FOR BUDGET PURPOSES

Total cost = Labour cost (+ machine cost) + chemical cost

e.g. area to be sprayed = 37.0 hectares
average distance between rows = 2.2 metres
average row length = 260 metres
swathe width of each atomizer = 1.2 metres

herbicide: atrazine to be applied at 10 litres/treated hectare plus water in ratio 1:1 to give 25 litres/treated hectare.

machine: tractor-mounted controlled drop applicator with two Herbi heads.

(a) Labour cost

From Output Guide XV/G12 (1976) para. 6.
Time per hectare for 250 m row length = 58.59 SM
Time per hectare for 300 m row length = 57.65 SM
Therefore, by interpolation, time per hectare for 260 m row length

$$= 58.59 - \frac{(58.89 - 57.65) \times 1}{5} \text{ SM}$$

= 58.59 - 0.19 SM
= 58.40 SM

At 4.51 pence per SM, the labour cost per ha is 58.40 x 4.51 pence
= £2.63

(b) Machine cost

From a) above, standard time per hectare = 58.40 SM

Hourly machine rates: tractor £1.40
sprayer £0.40
£1.80

Therefore machine cost per hectare = $\frac{58.40}{60.00}$ x £1.80 = £1.75

(c) Chemical cost

Volume of herbicide per treated hectare = 10 litres
cost/litre = £1.75 Therefore cost per treated hectare = £17.50
To convert to cost/plantation hectare, we use the ratio:
swathe width 1.2 = 0.545
row distance 2.2
Therefore cost per hectare = 0.545 x £17.50
= £9.54

(b)   Total cost
Therefore total cost per hectare = £2.63 + £1.75 + £9.54
= £13.92
and total cost = £13.92 x 37.0 = £515.40

Notes: 1.   Always be careful to calculate all resources in either plantation hectares or treated hectares and to adjust accordingly to reach the correct total.
2.   Managers should remember to add an allowance for oncost (insurance, holidays, wet-time, etc.) for directly employed labour when appropriate.

11°

12. LIST OF HERBICIDES AND THEIR MANUFACTURERS OR DISTRIBUTORS

	Herbicide	Manufacturer's or Distributor's Code No.
A	Ammonium sulphamate	2
B	Asulam	11
C	Atrazine	4, 8
D	Atrazine with Dalapon	1
E	2,4-D amine	9, 10, 12, 18
F	2,4-D ester	1A, 3, 5, 6, 11
G	Fosamine ammonium	16
H	Glyphosate	13
J	Hexazinone	16
K	Paraquat	15
L	Propyzamide	14, 17
M	2,4,5-T ester	10
N	Triclopyr	7

MANUFACTURERS OR DISTRIBUTORS OF APPROVED PRODUCTS

		Herbicide code letters
1.	Atlas Interlates Ltd., Fraser Road, Erith, Kent DA8 1PN Erith (032 24) 32255	D
1A.	BASF United Kingdom Ltd., Agrochemical Division, Lady Lane, Hadleigh, Ipswich, Suffolk IP7 6BQ Hadleigh (0473) 822531	F
2.	Battle, Hayward & Bower Ltd., Victoria Chemical Works, Crofton Drive, Allenby Road Industrial Estate, Lincoln LN3 4NP Lincoln (0522) 29206-7	A
3.	BP Oil Ltd., Crop Protection Dept., BP House, Victoria Street, London SW1E 5NJ 01-821 2787/2556	F

12

4.   Burts and Harvey   C
     Crabtree Manorway North, Belvedere, Kent
     DA17 6BQ
     01-311 7000

5.   J.D.Campbell & Sons Ltd. and J.D.Campbell   F
     (Sales) Ltd.
     18 Liverpool Road, Great Sankey, Warrington,
     Cheshire
     Warrington (0925) 33232-3

6.   J.W. Chafer Ltd., Chafer House, 19 Thorne Road,   F
     Doncaster, S. Yorks, DN1 2HQ
     Doncaster (0302) 67371

7.   Chipman Ltd., The Goods Yard, Horsham,   N
     Sussex RH12 2NR
     Horsham (0403) 60341-5

8.   Ciba-Geigy Agrochemicals, Whittlesford,   C
     Cambridge CB2 4QT
     Cambridge (0223) 833621-7

9.   Farm Protection Ltd., Glaston Park, Glaston,   E
     Oakham, Leicestershire LE15 9BX
     Uppingham (0572) 822561

10. A.H. Marks & Co. Ltd.,   EM
     Wyke Lane, Wyke, Bradford, W. Yorks
     BD12 9EJ
     Bradford (0274) 675231

11. May & Baker Ltd., Agrochemicals Division,   BF
     Regent House, Hubert Road, Brentwood, Essex
     CM14 4QQ
     Brentwood (0277) 230522

12. Mirfield Sales Services Ltd.,   E
     Moorend House, Moorend Lane, Dewsbury,
     W. Yorks WF13 4QQ
     Heckmondwike (0924) 409782

13. Monsanto Ltd., Agricultural Division,   H
     Thames Tower, Burleys Way, Leicester LE1 3TP
     Leicester (0533) 20864

14. Pan Britannica Industries Ltd.,   L
     Britannica House, Waltham Cross, Herts
     EN8 7DY
     Waltham Cross (0992) 23691

15. Plant Protection Division,   K
     Imperial Chemical Industries Ltd.,
     Fernhurst, Haslemere, Surrey GU27 3JE
     Haslemere (0428) 4061 (Technical advice:
     Farnham 0252-724525)

12

16. Selectokil Ltd.,   GJ
    Abbey Gate Place, Tovil, Maidstone, Kent
    Maidstone (0622) 55471

17. Shell Chemicals UK Ltd., Agricultural Division   L
    39-41 St Mary's Street, Ely, Cambs CB7 4HG
    Ely (0353) 3671

18. Universal Crop Protection Ltd.,   E
    Park House, Maidenhead Road, Cookham,
    Maidenhead, Berks SL6 9DS
    Bourne End (06285) 26083

12

13. GLOSSARY AND ABBREVIATIONS

13.1 ABBREVIATIONS USED IN THE TEXT

13.1.1 Species

	Common Name	Latin Name
CP	Corsican pine	*Pinus nigra* var. *maritima*
DF	Douglas fir	*Pseudotsuga menziesii*
EL	European larch	*Larix decidua*
GF	Grand fir	*Abies grandis*
LC	Lawson's cypress	*Chamaecyparis lawsoniana*
LP	Lodgepole pine	*Pinus contorta*
NF	Noble fir	*Abies procera*
NS	Norway spruce	*Picea abies*
OMS	Serbian spruce	*Picea omorika*
PDP	Ponderosa pine	*Pinus ponderosa*
RAP	Monterey pine	*Pinus radiata*
RC	Western red cedar	*Thuja plicata*
SP	Scots pine	*Pinus sylvestris*
SS	Sitka spruce	*Picea sitchensis*
WH	Western hemlock	*Tsuga heterophylla*

13.1.2 Other abbreviations and symbols

ACAS	Agricultural Chemicals Approval Scheme
a.e.	acid equivalent
a.i	active ingredient
BASIS	British Agrochemical Supply Industry Scheme Ltd.
CDBA	Controlled droplet band applicator (-tion)
CDIA	Controlled droplet incremental applicator (-tion)
cm	centimetre(s)
FC	Forestry Commission
FSC	Forestry Safety Council
g	gramme(s)
ha	hectare(s)
HV	High Volume
kg	kilogramme(s)
kph	kilometres per hour
l	litre(s)
LV	Low Volume
m	metre(s)
ml	millilitre(s)
mm	millimetre(s)
MV	Medium Volume
NRS	Northern Research Station (Forestry Commission, Research Division)
psi	pounds per square inch
PSPS	Pesticides Safety Precautions Scheme

13

rev.	revised
rpm	revolutions per minute
s(or sec)	second(s)
s.c.	suspension concentrate
SM	Standard Minutes
ULV	Ultra Low Volume
VLV	Very Low Volume
w.p.	wettable powder
w/v	weight per volume
w/w	weight per weight

13.2 GLOSSARY OF GENERAL AND TECHNICAL TERMS

Acid equivalent (a.e.) The amount of active ingredient expressed in terms of the parent acid.

Active ingredient (a.i.) That part of a herbicide formulation from which the phytotoxicity (weedkilling effect) is obtained.

Additive. A herbicidally inactive material which is added to a herbicide formulation to improve its performance in any way.

Adjuvant. A herbicidally inactive material which is added to a herbicide formulation to enhance the phytotoxicity (weedkilling effect) of the formulation.

Agitation. Continual mixing of a liquid preparation of a herbicide (usually at the stage of final dilution) by shaking or stirring.

Annulus. A ring or circular band.

Application method (or pattern). The spatial arrangement on a weeding site of the areas which receive an application of herbicide and the relationship of this pattern to the crop trees (when present). There is a close association between such a pattern and the application equipment used: the term 'application method' should strictly speaking refer to the applicator and its use as well as the application pattern produced.

Sub-divisions are:

Complete application. Herbicide applied uniformly over the whole weeding site.

Band application. Herbicide applied to a strip of ground or vegetation, normally centred on a row of crop trees.

Spot application. Herbicide applied to a small patch of ground or vegetation, normally immediately around a crop tree.

Stem or cut stump treatments. Herbicide applied to individual stems or cut stumps wherever they may occur on a weeding site (not necessarily over the whole site).

Overall spray. Herbicide sprayed over the top of the crop (as opposed to placed spray).

Placed spray. Any method or pattern of spraying which ensures that herbicide does not come into contact with the crop trees.

13

114

Directed spray. A type of placed spray (q.v.) where the spray is aimed towards the ground or surrounding vegetation so as to minimize the amount of herbicide deposited on the crop.

Guarded spray. A type of placed spray (q.v.) where the crop trees are physically protected from direct contact with the spray by a guard or guards, usually attached to the applicator.

Incremental drift. A form of complete application (q.v.) where herbicide is sprayed as discrete droplets small enough to be wind-assisted to their target and applied in successive overlapping bands so that a relatively even coverage of the whole ground area is achieved.

Applicator. A piece of equipment designed to distribute herbicide on to ground or vegetation.

Approved product. A herbicidal product of known efficacy approved for use in forestry either under the Agricultural Chemicals Approval Scheme or as a result of the Forestry Commission's own trials and research.

Band application. See Application method.

Calibration. The process of calculation, measurement and adjustment (of variables such as nozzle size, pressure, walking speed) by which the correct application rate is achieved.

Carrier. A liquid or solid material within which a herbicide is dispersed (e.g. solution or suspension) to facilitate application.

Chlorosis. Loss of green colour in plant foliage.

Coarse grasses. An imprecise term used to describe grasses of a generally tall, bulky, rank, stiff and often tussocky nature which are usually more resistant than normal to grass herbicides. By contrast the so-called soft grasses are usually more susceptible to grass herbicides.

Commercial clearance (more properly: **Full commercial clearance**). The status given to herbicidal (and other pesticidal) products which have fully satisfied all the requirements of the Pesticides Safety Precautions Scheme.

Contact herbicide. One that kills or injures plant tissue close to the point of entry into the plant. (Contrast with translocated herbicide.)

Controlled drop application (CDA). A term used loosely to describe spinning disc and other systems intended to produce spray droplets of uniform size.

Diluent. The liquid added to a herbicide concentrate to increase its volume to an extent suitable for application.

Direct applicator. A piece of equipment which transfers liquid herbicide to a weed by direct contact with no intervening passage of droplets in air.

Directed spray. See Application method.

13

Dormant period. The period of the year when the aerial part of a plant is not actively growing.

Emulsifiable concentrate. See Formulation.

Emulsion. A mixture in which fine globules of one liquid are dispersed in another, e.g. oil in water.

Esters and salts. Different groups of compounds derived from an organic acid. Esters are normally oil-soluble while salts are more usually water-soluble.

Fine droplets. Droplets of a liquid preparation of herbicide which are comparatively small in diameter and which are therefore liable to drift during application.

Flushing. The commencement of growth of a plant above ground, characterised by sap flow and swelling and bursting of buds. Flushing follows the end of dormancy and marks the beginning of the growing season.

Formulation:

(i) The process of preparing a herbicide in a form suitable for practical use either neat or after dilution.

(ii) The material resulting from the above process. Types of formulation are:

> **Emulsifiable concentrate.** A concentrated solution of a herbicide and an emulsifier in an organic solvent which will form an emulsion on mixing with water.
>
> **Granules.** A free flowing dry preparation of herbicide (in a solid carrier in the form of particles within a given diameter range) which is ready to use.
>
> **Liquid.** A concentrated solution of a herbicide which mixes readily with water.
>
> **Suspension concentrate.** A stable suspension of a solid herbicide in a fluid, intended for dilution before use.
>
> **ULV formulation.** Herbicide in a special blend of oils intended for application through a rotary atomizer without dilution.
>
> **Wettable powder.** Herbicide in a powder so formulated that it will form a suspension when mixed with water.

Herbi. Trade name of a controlled droplet applicator.

Herbicide. A chemical which can kill or damage a plant.

Hormonal action. The mode of action of certain herbicides (e.g. 2,4,5-T) which achieve their effect by interfering with the growth regulatory mechanisms of the weed plant. Bending, curling and deformation (epinasty) of shoots and leaves is a common symptom of such effects.

Incremental drift. See Application method.

Liquid formulation. See Formulation.

Low-volatile ester. An ester of an organic acid (e.g. 2,4,5-T) which has a sufficiently long chain of carbon atoms in the molecule to reduce the amount that evaporates during and after spraying to an insignificant level.

13

Low volume. See Volume rate.

Medium volume. See Volume rate.

Nozzle types. Nozzles for liquid herbicide applicators are described by the spray distribution pattern produced:

    Fan. Spray droplets are emitted in a fan shape which distributes an elongated oval pattern on the ground. Overlapping of the tapered edges will produce an even distribution.

    Even fan. Spray droplets are emitted in a flat fan shape which distributes a long narrow parallel-sided band pattern on the ground.

    Hollow cone. Spray droplets are emitted in the shape of a hollow cone which produces an annulus on the ground.

    Anvil flooding. Spray droplets are emitted in a wide fan by striking the stream of herbicide against a dispersing surface (the anvil) to produce a wide band pattern on the ground.

    Solid stream. Herbicide is emitted as a continuous jet and not broken down into separate droplets. Droplet formation may take place in mid air depending on the length of the trajectory and the initial turbulence of the stream of fluid.

    Variable. A nozzle in which the distribution of spray can be adjusted from a narrow jet to a wide cone pattern.

Overall spray. See Application method.

Pepperpot. A simple (often home-made) hand-held container with holes drilled in the lid for distribution of granular herbicides.

Pesticide. A generic term covering herbicides, fungicides, insecticides, etc.

Photosynthetic process. The series of chemical reactions in the plant leaf by which sugar is made from carbon dioxide, water and sunlight. Some herbicides achieve their effect by interfering with one or more of these reactions.

Placed spray. See Application method.

Poisons Rules. Regulations governing the labelling, storage and sale of materials listed as poisons under the Poisons Act 1972. See Section 1.5.

Post-planting. After the crop is planted.

Pre-planting. Before the crop is planted.

Product. A formulation of a herbicide of fixed (but usually confidential) composition and of known strength (% content of the active ingredient or acid equivalent) which is commercially marketed under a particular brand name.

Rate of application. The amount (weight or volume) of active ingredient or of product applied per unit area, per plant, per incision, etc. Because of the range of possible meanings, confusion should be avoided by quoting the appropriate units, e.g. litres of product per treated hectare.

Residual herbicide. One which remains active in the soil for a period after it has been applied.

13

Resistant. Unaffected or undamaged by exposure to a herbicide applied at a stated rate. Usually used to describe the reaction of weed species to a herbicide.

Restock area. An area where one forest crop has been clear felled and is being replaced directly by another.

Rotary atomizer. A herbicide applicator in which the herbicide liquid is broken into droplets of a more or less uniform diameter by being thrown from the edge of a spinning disc.

Selective herbicide. One which, if used appropriately, will kill or damage some plant species while leaving others unaffected.

Senescence. The annual ageing process by which each autumn the leaves or above-ground parts of plants wither and die back.

Sensitive. Easily damaged by a herbicide.

Setting bud. The formation of buds in readiness for the next season's growth. Usually follows closely after the end of the season's rapid growth and the development of a waxy cuticle.

Soft (or fine) grasses. See Coarse grasses.

Soil-acting herbicide. One which is active through the soil, usually entering plants through the roots.

Spot application. See Application method.

Stem treatment. See Application method.

Surfactant (or Surface-active agent). A substance which is added to a spray solution to reduce the surface tension of the liquid and increase the emulsifying, spreading and wetting properties.

Susceptible. Easily damaged by a herbicide applied at a stated rate.

Suspension. Particles dispersed through (but not dissolved in) a liquid.

Suspension concentrate. See Formulation.

Swath(e). A strip of ground or vegetation of a given width which receives herbicide from a single pass of an applicator.

Tolerant. Unaffected or undamaged by exposure to a herbicide. Usually used to describe the reaction of crop trees to a selective herbicide.

Total herbicide. A herbicide used in such a way as to kill all vegetation.

Toxicity. The capacity of a material to produce any noxious effect - reversible or irreversible - on the body.

Translocated herbicide. One which is moved within the plant and can affect parts of the plant remote from the point of application.

Treated area. The area of ground or plantation that is actually covered with herbicide. (Usually expressed as treated hectares).

Ultra low volume. See Volume rate.

Very low volume. See Volume rate.

Volume rate. The amount of spray solution (diluent plus herbicide) applied per unit area. Volume rates are frequently described as high, medium, low, very low or ultra-low volume but several conventions exist as to the range of rates to which each term refers. The definitions used in this Booklet are to be found in Section 11.1.1 but where precision is important it is advisable to state the exact rate.

13

Weed spectrum. The range of undesirable species which are killed or adequately controlled by a herbicide.

Wettable powder. See Formulation.

Wetting or wetting agent. A surfactant (q.v.).

Weight per volume (w/v). A means of expressing the amount of active ingredient in a commercial formulation by relating this amount, by weight, to the volume of the formulation. In expressing the ratio as a percentage, the assumption is made that 1.0 litre of every formulation weighs 1.0 kg (e.g. 20% w/v = 0.2 kg in every litre of formulation).

Weight per weight (w/w). A means of expressing the amount of active ingredient in a commercial formulation by relating this amount, weight by weight, to the weight of the formulation (e.g. 20% w/w = 0.2 kg in every 1.0 kg of formulation).

13

INDEX TO WEEDS AND CHEMICALS

14

14

Enquiries relating to this publication should be addressed to the Publications Officer, Forestry Commission Research Station, Alice Holt Lodge, Wrecclesham, Farnham, Surrey GU10 4LH.

14